health
for life 1

A TEACHER'S PLANNING GUIDE TO
HEALTH EDUCATION IN THE PRIMARY SCHOOL

Project team:

Trefor Williams

Noreen Wetton

Alysoun Moon

HEALTH EDUCATION AUTHORITY

THE HEALTH EDUCATION AUTHORITY'S PRIMARY SCHOOL PROJECT

Nelson

These materials are the outcome of a four-year Health Education Authority project based at the University of Southampton and undertaken in association with the HEA Schools Health Education Unit at the University of Exeter.

Thomas Nelson and Sons Ltd
Nelson House   Mayfield Road
Walton-on-Thames   Surrey
KT12 5PL   UK

51 York Place
Edinburgh
EH1 3JD   UK

Thomas Nelson (Hong Kong) Ltd
Toppan Building 10/F
22A Westlands Road
Quarry Bay   Hong Kong

Distributed in Australia by

Thomas Nelson Australia
102 Dodds Street
South Melbourne   Victoria 3205
and in Sydney, Brisbane, Adelaide and Perth

Nelson Canada
1120 Birchmount Road
Scarborough Ontario
M1K 5G4   Canada

© Health Education Authority 1989
First published by Thomas Nelson and Sons Ltd 1989

All photographs by John Walmsley
Phototypeset and illustrated by Gecko Limited, Bicester, Oxon.

Illustrations by Gecko Limited and Nirava Kavya

ISBN 0-17-423111-3

NPN   987654

Printed in Hong Kong

Contents

List of themes

This is a list of themes for which activities are provided in this book. There are of course many more themes to be tackled in health education, some of which are suggested at the beginning of each age section. There is more material on relationships, drugs and keeping safe in *Health for Life 2* (see Appendix 2, page 181).

Using this planning guide

This guide has been written to help you and your colleagues plan a health education programme for the primary years using the healthy lifestyles approach. As every school has different priorities, the aim of Part One is to help *you* to organise your own programme in a way that is best for your school. It will also be very helpful for Health Education Officers and others who run courses and workshops for teachers, and much of the material has been used on such courses. Although this might be the ideal way to tackle health education, some of you may want health education teaching material which you can use immediately, and the classroom strategies and activities in Part Two fulfil this need. These are provided for four age ranges: 4 and 5, 6 and 7, 8 and 9 and 10 and 11, and have all been used successfully in the classroom. They can either be used as they stand, or modified, or combined with your own materials. Above all the aim of this guide is to be flexible.

In the accompanying book, *Health for Life 2 – Health education in the primary school: A teacher's guide to three key topics*, you will find more activities for the key themes, Keeping myself safe, Me and my relationships and The world of drugs, which you can use in addition to those in this book.

The book is in two parts:

Part One ● ***Setting the Scene***

Part One is designed to help you decide on the kind of health education programme your school needs and how to organise it. It is divided into three chapters:

- **What is the healthy lifestyle approach?**

  This explains how the approach was devised from the results of research into children's attitudes to health.

- **The school as a health-promoting community**

  This chapter argues that successful health education should not be confined to the classroom but should involve the whole school, the children's families and the community. Photocopiable worksheets are provided to make it easier for you to discuss these issues with colleagues and parents in a 'workshop' situation.

- **Deciding on the content of your health education programme**

  This helps you to organise health issues and topics into a programme and to decide how health education can be fitted into your primary curriculum. More worksheets are provided.

Part Two ● *Into Action*

Part Two is designed to help you begin teaching health topics. It consists of:

- **The Scope and Sequence Chart**

  This is a flexible framework for planning health education for 4–11 year olds which can be modified according to the needs of your school. It suggests issues and topics which can be tackled at each age, and reflects a spiral curriculum in that themes are revisited and extended as the children progress through school.

- **A user's guide to the Scope and Sequence Chart**

- **Four Action Planners for four age ranges: 4 and 5, 6 and 7, 8 and 9, and 10 and 11.**

  These provide starting points for planning activities, and consist of 'content boxes' which can be used in any order to provide ideas for single lessons or a series of lessons.

- **A user's guide to the Action Planners**

- **Classroom strategies and activities for the four age ranges**

  These are based on content boxes from the Action Planners. Activities are provided for key themes for each age range. Opportunities for cross-curricular work and family involvement are also highlighted.

- **Classroom strategies and activities – a summary**

  Talking, creative writing, presentation and display and role-play are some of the strategies discussed.

Appendices

- **1 The Draw and Write Investigation Technique**

  This is one method for finding out how children perceive and explain health matters. Ideally this should be carried out before you begin to explore themes with them.

- **2 Resources**

  A list of books and materials for reference.

Part One
Setting the scene

What is the healthy lifestyles approach?

● ***The starting point: children's perceptions of health***

At the heart of this approach is a commitment to discovering what children perceive a healthy lifestyle to be, and using this as a starting point for planning their health education programme.

In particular, it is important to find out

— what they think they do to be, and stay, healthy;

— what they think other people do to be, and stay, healthy;

— and why they do these things.

Three investigations*, involving 22,603 children across 11 LEAs, provided baseline information for the healthy lifestyles approach. The investigations revealed

— more about the children's changing perceptions of health and healthy lifestyles;

— the holistic view children have of the world and of being and staying healthy: •

— their growing ability to make strong connections between what they do and being and staying healthy;

— their ability to evaluate their own and other people's lifestyles and pinpoint changes they might need to make;

— which of a given range of health related topics children were most interested in and which topics they wanted to learn more about;

— what parents, teachers and health professionals thought were the most important of a given range of topics, and when they thought different topics should be introduced.

● ***A flexible framework for planning***

A flexible framework is needed because

— the National Curriculum places responsibility on schools to make provision for health education through the foundation subjects;

— different schools and their communities will have different needs, priorities and interests;

— new issues, information and areas of concern will emerge and new responses will be needed. Lifestyles will change.

The healthy lifestyles approach builds on children's perceptions, and their growing skills and abilities to provide a flexible framework for planning and teaching a health education programme. As a result the programme should enable the children to evaluate different lifestyles and eventually adopt a suitable one for themselves.

The diagram below represents the successive stages in children's health education as they learn to evaluate healthy lifestyles using this approach. They begin by learning to make connections between their actions (and/or what others do for them) and their health. They progress to learning about and evaluating other people's lifestyles, and eventually arrive at the point where they can consciously adopt their own lifestyle and take responsibility for their own decisions.

Learning to evaluate healthy lifestyles – especially my own.

Ages

4-5 What do people around me do to keep me healthy? What do I do to help them?

6 My healthy day: what happens? What do I do? What do others do to and for me?

7 Other people's healthy days? How do they differ from mine? Who and what keeps them healthy? Who and what keeps me healthy?

8-9 What makes other people's lifestyles healthy – and not so healthy? How does my lifestyle measure up? What do I need to know?

10-11 What makes a healthy lifestyle for me, now and in the future? What are the pressures? How do I judge my lifestyle? How do others judge it? What changes can I make?

* a D T Williams, N M Wetton, A M H Moon, *A Picture of Health – What do you do that makes you healthy and keeps you healthy?* (Health Education Authority, 1989). (This investigation used the Draw and Write Investigation Technique described in Appendix 1, page 176.)

b D T Williams, N M Wetton, A M H Moon, *A Way In – Five Key Areas of Health Education,* (Health Education Authority, 1989).

c J W Balding, *Just-a-Tick – A Personal Development and Health Education Enquiry,* (HEA Schools Health Education Unit, Exeter University, 1986).

These investigations formed the early phase of the Primary Project 1985–86.

The school as a health-promoting community

• *What is a health-promoting school?*

School health education has traditionally concentrated on children's knowledge, attitudes and behaviour, with little attention to the wider social and familial influences. Our research has shown how important it is for what is taught in the classroom to be supported and reinforced by the ethos of the school itself, as well as by families and the wider community, for example, community workers, health and safety professionals and the school meals service. Children are naturally confused when what they are taught is not seen to be practised outside the classroom, and although it is impossible to protect them completely from conflicting values and behaviour, a health-promoting school can minimise these conflicts and confusions by supporting its health education programme through its ethos and in all aspects of school life.

It is up to you and your colleagues to decide what characterises a health-promoting school and what changes are needed in your school to make it more health-promoting. The following photocopiable worksheets (1–3) are designed to help you to do this.

Each sheet takes as its theme a frequently-asked question. On the reverse of the sheets you will find some of the responses often given by teachers and health professionals who have been involved in 'health-promoting school' workshops. You may find it interesting to compare these with your own responses, or use them as a basis for discussion.

You will find that these sheets can be used in many different ways, for example,

— for your own interest and for clarifying your own views;

— as a starting point for informal and formal discussion with other teachers in your school or feeder schools;

— as a starting point for discussion with wider groups, such as, parents, governors and health professionals who share your concern and responsibility for children's health and health education;

— as a starting point for school-based research and development.

Worksheet 1a

What would you expect to find in a health-promoting school?

I would expect to find . . .

Worksheet 1b

What would you expect to find in a health-promoting school? Some typical responses.

I would expect to find . . .

. . . care for each individual child and adult

. . . real consultation

. . . a healthy building

. . . policies about specific issues, for example: smoking, school meals, tuck shop

. . . people being valued and valuing each other

. . . confident and happy children

. . . a happy atmosphere

. . . a stimulating atmosphere

. . . a planned health education curriculum

. . . the fostering of responsibility and independence

Worksheet 2a

What issues would you expect to have been considered in a health-promoting school?

I would expect the school to have considered . . .

Worksheet 2b

What issues would you expect to have been considered in a health-promoting school? Some typical responses.

I would expect the school to have considered . . .

. . . ways of fostering responsibility and independence

. . . how children develop and promote their own and others' self-esteem

. . . the need for a welcoming and stimulating physical environment

. . . sensitive issues relating to drugs, sex education, aids, child abuse

. . . the importance of good relationships

. . . the need to build strong links with home, community and health professionals

. . . the need to go out into the community and draw the community into the school

. . . how to promote the safety of children in its care

. . . the need for opportunities, for taking risks and for excitement

. . . issues about food, smoking, bullying

. . . the need for a supportive environment for staff and families

Worksheet 3a

What kind of health education curriculum would you expect to find in a health-promoting school?

I would expect to find a health education curriculum which . . .

Worksheet 3b

What kind of health education curriculum would you expect to find in a health-promoting school? Some typical responses.

I would expect to find a health education curriculum which . . .

. . . reaches out into the home and family and values their contribution

. . . starts from the children's standpoint, and uses the experiences they bring to their learning

. . . is relevant, taking account of different backgrounds, beliefs and concerns

. . . is active, developing a range of early study skills and life skills

. . . is sufficiently flexible to respond to children's needs at different times

. . . has in-built progression

. . . can be built into the day-to-day school curriculum

. . . is reinforced by the ethos of the school

. . . sets realistic goals

. . . is re-evaluated and changed as appropriate

Three tasks for the development of a health-promoting school

By the time you reach this section of the guide you should already have an idea of what you believe a health-promoting school to be. Also it should be clear that the tasks involved in developing such a school go further than the creation of a health education curriculum. You will now be able to consider the potential of your school as a health-promoting community, and will be able to identify what could be done and the changes you would like to make.

To help you start, three tasks are outlined on the following worksheets (4–6). Each school will see these tasks differently according to its needs and priorities, and will carry them out in its own way, so there is space left on the worksheets for you to note down what they will mean for your school. The tasks are interdependent and it is important that they are shared with all those concerned with the health of the children so as to draw upon all the available skills, knowledge and support.

Worksheet 4

Building a health-promoting ethos

What is involved in this task?	What will it mean for our school?
Working towards a stimulating, clean, safe, healthy environment	....
Supporting the taught curriculum	....
Supporting children and their families	....
Supporting the school staff	....
Supporting the school health service	....
Preparing children for the real world	....
Setting up networks of support with health professionals, social workers and LEA advisers	....

Is there anything more we can do?

....

....

....

....

....

Worksheet 5

Reaching out to families and the community

Photocopy

What is involved in this task?	What does it mean for our school?
Consulting	....
Negotiating	....
Informing	....
Asking for support	....
Drawing on the skills and expertise of families and the community	....
Taking children out into the community – the *real* world	....
Extending school based work into the family	....

Is there anything more we can do?

....
....
....
....
....

Worksheet 6

Planning and implementing a flexible health education programme

Things to do	What might be involved?	What will it mean for our school?
Organise and manage all the different topic areas which make up a health education programme	Using a flexible planning framework which enables a balanced progressive programme to be put into action (see the next chapter)	
Find out what perceptions children have and the experiences they can bring to their learning	Using simple classroom techniques (see Appendix 1, page 176) to discover children's perceptions of healthy lifestyles.	
Ensure each child feels valued and use valid learning experiences, activities and materials for all the children	Exploring active learning strategies and questioning some accepted methods, for example, colouring in or gap filling	
Consult with all those concerned with your health education programme	Planning informal discussions and workshops for the adults, as well as using the classroom techniques mentioned above to ascertain the children's views.	
Be aware of the latest issues, trends and concerns	Keeping up to date with current issues revealed by research findings and the media, the views of parents and the community, and the recommendations of the DES and LEAs.	
Know when, where and how to seek support and professional guidance, and set up partnerships and networks	Initiating contact with relevant groups and individuals. This could include holding 'open' workshop sessions; involving the school nurse; using local and national resources such as Health Education Officers, The Health Education Authority and safety organisations (see Appendix 2, page 181)	

Deciding on the content of your health education programme

Many of the activities outlined in the previous chapter will only be accomplished in the long term. But the immediate exercise is to devise a relevant health education programme for your school which is sufficiently flexible to take account of present needs and long term plans. Initial decisions have to be made concerning the content of the programme, what is to be taught, when and how it is to be taught, and how that learning and teaching is to fit into an already crowded curriculum. To help you make the right decisions for your school, this exercise has been divided into three tasks.

Managing and organising the content of the programme

How do you decide what to teach? You might like to try developing a list of topics with a group of colleagues through a brainstorming session. Alternatively, you could start with the list on Worksheet 7, page 17 (which is typical of the lists resulting from such sessions) add the topics you think have been left out and delete those which you feel don't belong there. You will probably find that at the end of the session you have a very long, all-embracing list. This will probably not remain static but will change over time as new concerns arise.

The next job is to organise these topics into a coherent health education programme. Different schools will have different ways of tackling this, but one way is to group them into three content areas which will provide the foundations for a broadly-based health education programme:

- *Me and looking after myself*
  All key topics concerned with the present and future health of my body and its safety.

- *Me and my relationships*
  All key topics concerned with my relationships.

- *Me and my community and environment*
  All key topics concerned with my place in the community and my awareness of the environment.

Organising content in this way will help you to tackle day-to-day health topics, key areas of concern and sensitive issues without any of them becoming isolated or over-emphasised. It will also help you to plan the scope and sequence of the whole programme.

You could now try, as a second workshop activity, grouping all the topics in your list into these three content areas using Worksheet 8 on page 18. There is no clear-cut way to do this, and it is likely that members of your group will have differing opinions about the direction that should be taken. You may find that some topics can be grouped into more than one area, and that topics from all three content areas can be grouped together to form key themes. It is worth making a note of these for when you plan your classroom work.

Identifying priorities and key themes

As you start to organise the content of the programme priorities will become clear. These may include key themes which apply to specific ages or stages of development, and the special needs and concerns of your school. You could now try another workshop activity: deciding on the priorities for your class using Worksheet 9 on page 19 to help you. Group the priorities under the content headings as you did with the topics, and decide on the main focus and content of your teaching.

At this point it is worth noting opportunities for work with families, and potential links between specific health topic areas and other subjects in the curriculum. However, these priorities and themes must be integrated into your overall plan, it is important not to lose sight of the scope and sequence of your programme as it extends throughout the primary age range.

Incorporating health education into the primary school curriculum

The problem facing you at this stage is how to fit health education into an already packed primary school curriculum. Worksheet 10 on page 20 summarises six strategies which will enable you to do this (no doubt you are already using some of them). The advantages and possible disadvantages of each strategy are given as a guide to their effectiveness, to indicate how they might be used in combination and to show the limitations of using just one strategy exclusively.

You can use this worksheet

— as the starting point for a workshop discussion;

— to review the ways in which health education is incorporated into the curriculum of your school;

— to look at alternative models for planning;

— to share with other professionals and groups outside the school the ways in which health education crosses curriculum boundaries.

Worksheet 7

Managing and organising the content of the programme: some topics to consider.

nits   sexuality   posture   digestion   leisure

germs   relationships   attitudes

exercise

people who help us   conservation   dental health   AIDS

pets   food   growth

media pressure   loss and death   puberty

feelings   gender

how my body works   helping others   sex

growing up   fresh air

growing   discrimination   coping with conflict

road safety   friendships   bullying

keeping myself safe   care of eyes

infection   smoking   drugs   first aid   rest

healthy heart   child abuse   clothing   pollution

water safety   senses   immunisation

caring   vandalism   menstruation

separation   hair   using the health service

Worksheet 8

Managing and organising the programme content – grouping the topics into three content areas

Photocopy

Me and looking after myself	Me and my relationships	Me and my community and environment
All key topics concerned with the present and future health of my body and its safety	All key topics concerned with my relationships	All key topics concerned with my place in the community and my awareness of the environment

Priority themes for my class/year group

- ....
- ....
- ....

Worksheet 9 • Identifying priorities and key themes

Me and looking after myself	Me and my relationships	Me and my community and environment

PRIORITIES

FOCUS AND CONTENT

Worksheet 10

Incorporating health education into the primary school curriculum

Photocopy

Strategies	Advantages	Possible disadvantages
1 Tackling health education topics incidentally as they arise	Provides an immediate and relevant response to changing interests and needs	Health education may never happen
2 Using one-off activities, visitors and visits	These can be used as starting points for new learning	Impact may only be short term
3 Giving health education a regular, separate slot in the curriculum	Allows for systematic planning Makes use of specialist talents, TV programmes and outside support	Health education could be isolated
4 Exploring health education through project work, either as part of another project or as a project in itself	A way of integrating health with other subjects Good for tackling current issues	Health education messages could be manipulated to fit the project
5 Combining health education with one or two other subject areas such as science or PE	Gives health education focus Allows for planned progression Could be the starting point for a wider cross-curricular approach	Health education messages could be narrowed
6 Integrating health education into all subjects across the curriculum, looking for those curriculum areas best suited to each theme	A flexible approach which can be adapted to take advantage of on-going activites A way of reinforcing health messages across the curriculum	Health education could be pushed out by other demands

Part Two
Into action

A user's guide to the scope and sequence chart

The Scope and Sequence Chart is a non-prescriptive framework which will help you to plan a health education programme which is flexible enough to respond to the concerns of your school and community. The focus is on healthy lifestyles and what these mean to children as they move through the primary school.

You can use this chart in a number of different ways for both short- and long-term planning. For example you can use it

— as a starting point for developing a whole school policy on health education (discussed earlier in the chapter on health-promoting schools);

— for reviewing this policy;

— to record what has been taught in order to avoid non-productive repetition (and ensure the continuity of the spiral curriculum);

— as a starting point for consultation with all those concerned with children's education in health;

— as a basis for discussion with feeder schools and schools to which the children will eventually go.

There are three main strands in the chart which run across the whole primary age range (4–11):

1 Children's changing perceptions of healthy lifestyles

2 Suggested programme content

3 Skills and strategies

Each of these strands is an essential component of a successful health education programme. They should be used and adapted according to the needs of your school and community.

1 *Children's changing perceptions of healthy lifestyles*

This strand gives an overview of children's changing perceptions of what they do to make and keep themselves healthy. (It was compiled using the results of the investigations mentioned on page 3). The best starting point for exploring any topic area with children is to use their own perceptions and explanations and a classroom technique for investigating these is provided in Appendix 1 (see page 176). This technique can also be used for monitoring changes in children's perceptions as they work through the programme you have planned. Once you have the results of your investigation you can avoid any conflict between what children bring to their learning and the learning experiences they are offered. You will be able to see what the children think they know about health, and what you can build on and what you should question.

2 *Suggested content and themes*

This strand suggests a range of starting points and themes which can be explored with the children. These are based on the three content areas discussed earlier: *Me and looking after myself, Me and my relationships* and *Me and my community and environment*. The themes are developed step-by-step through the age range as all new learning is based upon previous work.

This strand covers the following key topics which provide you with opportunities to tackle sensitive issues:

Me and my relationships	The world of drugs
Keeping myself safe	Exercise and rest
Healthy eating	How my body works

The world of drugs, Me and my relationships and Keeping myself safe are explored in greater detail in the accompanying book, *Health for Life 2 – Health Education in the primary school: a teacher's guide to three key topics*.

3 *Skills and strategies*

This strand summarises

- some of the skills which will enable children to explore their own perceptions and make sense of, and put into practice, new health information;

- a wide range of classroom strategies which you can adapt and extend. These are described more fully on pages 172–4.

As the skills and needs of different children of the same age vary, the content, skills work and strategies suggested on the chart for each age are only to be used as a guide – the children you teach may benefit from work suggested for other ages. This is something to think about before you turn to the more detailed framework provided by the four Action Planners which follow later in the book.

The Scope and Sequence Chart provides you with a basis for discussion and planning, now it is up to you to adapt it for your own use. You might find the following checklist useful:

- Will the plan respond to the needs of our school and the way we work?

- Can we use the suggested topics as they stand?
  What would we want to add or change?
  For more about how to tackle this, turn to page 15.

- How will the outlined skills and strategies work for classes in our school?
  Detailed descriptions of activities are provided on pages 30–171.

- How does the overview of children's perceptions compare with those of our children?
  An investigation technique to help you is provided in Appendix 1 on page 176.

Scope and Sequence Chart

Age	Children's changing perceptions of healthy lifestyles	Suggested programme content	Suggested skills practice
4 & 5	We don't all know what being healthy means but we think being healthy is being happy, being loved, and being with family	Exploring healthy, happy lifestyles	Choosing
		What does being healthy mean to me? What is it like to feel healthy?	Sharing
			Turn-taking
			Language skills
	We think healthy people (including us) keep healthy with – food – exercise – play	How do my actions affect how I feel?	Playing a role, distinguishing between reality and fantasy
		Growing and growing up	Linking action to outcomes
		Looking after myself, and keeping safe	Learning to value self, others and the environment
6 & 7	More of us know what is meant by 'being healthy'	Why do different people have different healthy lifestyles?	Making choices, saying 'Yes' and 'No'
	We think a healthy lifestyle involves – exercise and food – play – good relationships – work	What is my healthy lifestyle?	Working with others
		Outside and inside my body	Language skills
		Family, friends, sharing, caring	Investigation skills
			Exploring roles
	We're starting to realise – health care – hygiene – fresh air are important	Keeping safe and being responsible	Linking actions to outcomes
			Extending valuing skills

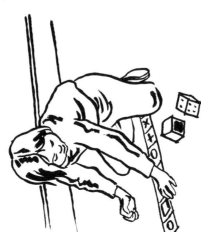

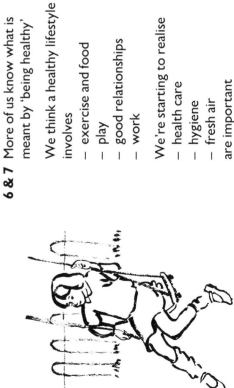

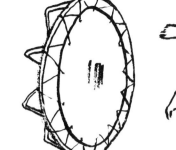

8 & 9 Our view of health is widening

We are beginning to understand how exercise and food affects our bodies and how we look and feel

Some of us see exercise more in terms of fitness, some of us are more aware of the importance of food

We are beginning to see why adults emphasise hygiene and sleep

Being with our friends is of growing importance

With growing independence comes a list of 'dos' and 'don'ts'

We are confused about the gap between what people say and what they do

Food and exercise for some of us is much more to do with how we look, for others, exercise means games and being fit and food is part of this

---

10 & 11

We have to deal with
— greater freedom
— greater peer support and interaction
— more rules
— more 'do's' and 'don'ts'

Our view of healthy lifestyles continues to widen

We are more aware of the large variety of things that contribute to a healthy lifestyle

Some of us are more aware of the value of medication but see drugs as a hazard

We are beginning to understand the need for regular exercise but some of us see it in terms of
— power
— strength
— achievement

Some of us link it with looking good

A healthy lifestyle is as much to do with 'don'ts' as 'do's'

How do my body and brain work, grow and change? What can I do to keep myself healthy, happy and safe?

What makes me feel good about myself, my friends and my family?

How can I help to keep my environment clean, safe and healthy?

Caring for others. Who are the carers?

Relationships and responsibility: friends, friendship and influences

Other people's lifestyles. My lifestyle — my choice

Understanding growing up

Hazards to healthy living

A more scientific approach to exercise, food and hygiene, and its quality, quantity and timing

Changing and growing: physically and emotionally

What's happening to me and other children? Exploring individual variations in growth.

Friends and friendship: understanding relationships and trust

What responsibility do I have for myself and those around me?

Evaluating the influence of the media

Developing a more scientific approach to the environment

The community

Leisure

Making decisions and choices
— responding to pressures and influences
— linking what you know to what you do

Working in and as a group

Language skills

Investigation skills: planning and summarising

Imitating roles and role-play

Linking action to outcome: critical moments and alternative solutions

Extending valuing skills

Practical skills: personal safety, personal hygiene

Making healthy choices and decisions: linking actions, outcomes and alternatives

Coping with media and peer pressure, both positive and negative

Handling conflict, recognising and responding to potentially difficult situations

Group skills and leadership

Language skills

Role-play

Extending valuing skills, relationship skills and responsibility

Practical skills: personal safety and personal hygiene

Investigation skills: organising and planning, researching, fact finding, collecting, collating, presenting, evaluating and weighing evidence

How exercise, food and hygiene contribute to a healthy lifestyle

How can I promote my own and others' health

Hazards to health

Sex roles and discrimination

Adolescent lifestyles in other cultures

Changing and growing

Motivation: putting knowledge into practice

Understanding my emotions

Maintaining a bodily equilibrium

Strategies

- Starting from children's perceptions
- Talking, telling and listening
- Writing
- Creative interpretation
- Playing and role-playing
- Using literature
- Using scientific investigations
- Using visits, visitors and TV programmes
- Using presentation and display
- Becoming an expert: passing on the message
- Family links

In this book you will find four Action Planners: one for each of the age ranges 4 and 5, 6 and 7, 8 and 9, and 10 and 11. Each Action Planner consists of 30–40 content boxes each on a different aspect of healthy lifestyles. These are written from the child's viewpoint. The content boxes are arranged under the now familiar three content area headings: *Me and looking after myself*, *Me and my relationships* and *Me and my community and environment*.

The content boxes can be linked thematically, usually two or three at a time, and provide starting points for exploring the theme in the classroom. At this point, you can *either*, decide on your own themes and select the content boxes you feel are appropriate for exploring them (if you wish to do this move on or to the section on planning your own themes below); *or*, you can turn to the Classroom Strategies and Activities chapters where you will find that content boxes for some key themes have already been selected for you.

Planning your own themes

Start by opening up the Action Planner for the age range you are teaching, and read through the content boxes. If you have worked through the workshop activities in Part One, you will already have decided on your key themes or priorities, and as you read through the content boxes you will begin to identify which ones are appropriate for your themes. It is a good idea to choose content boxes from each of the three content areas, so your theme is tackled from all three important perspectives. Make a list of the numbers of the content boxes you would like to use (the boxes are only numbered to make it easier for you to make a note of the ones you have chosen, and do not indicate order of use or priority). Decide the order in which you want to use the boxes. The boxes can be used, or re-used at different times in different themes.

Next, decide on the classroom strategies and activities you want to use. To help you do this some strategies and activities for each age range are provided in the following chapters, and a summary of strategies suitable for health education are provided on page 172. If you wish to organise your own activities remember which health messages you need to put across to the children. In order to do this effectively you need to consider the children's own perceptions of the theme, the views of their families, the community and health professionals. It is useful to keep in mind any special events going on in school, for example, visitors or visits, in case you can incorporate them. You should also think about the cross-curricular links you can make between health education and other subjects. With some themes it can be particularly helpful if the children's families can be involved in some of the activities. The following worksheet consists of a checklist to help you plan your themes, it is also a useful basis for staffroom or workshop discussions.

Worksheet 11

Planning a theme

- Theme to develop ....

....

- Using content boxes ....

- Starting point ....

- Key messages to put across ....

   ....

   ....

   ....

- Possible messages from
  – the children ....

   – the home ....

   – the community ....

   – the media ....

   – other sources ....

- Cross-curricular links ....

- Family work and involvement ....

....

- Possible strategies and classroom activities ....

....

- Resources and support needed ....

....

....

4&5

Action planner
Me & looking after myself

1. This body of mine: how do I think it looks? What parts can I see? How is it like your body? How is it different from your body and other people's bodies?

2. What goes *onto* my body? Who puts it there? For example, soap, water, shampoo, dirt, paint, ointment, plasters, sun, air, clothing, shoes.

3. What goes *into* my body? Who puts it there? For example food, drink, medicine, pills, air, dust, smoke, smells. How does it get in? How does it make me feel? Where do I think it goes?

4. What things can I do when I feel good and healthy? For example, run, play, laugh, go out.

5. What can't I do when I am feeling ill or not so healthy? How do I feel? What do I say and do?

6. What do I think I do to make and keep myself healthy? My healthy day: what do I do? For example, eat, sleep, exercise, play, get fresh air, keep myself clean. What do I think healthy people do or don't do?

7. How do I know I am growing? What can I reach? What can I do now? Which parts of me are growing? What size and shape are people? What size and shape am I? For example, small, middle-sized, tall.

8. What do I think made me grow? Who helped me to grow?

9. What do I *do* (everyday or sometimes) and what do other people do to my body to keep it healthy?

10. What do I think I have to keep safe from? How do I think I do this? What real and pretend things should I keep safe from?

11. What can I do for myself now that I couldn't do before?

What are the words I need to know to talk about:

– the parts of my body, both *my* words and the 'grown-up' words?
– real and pretend?
– size and shape?
– same and different?

– medicines, injections, pills and treatment?
– dangerous and safe?
– growing and growing up?
– asking for help?

Classroom strategies and activities for ages 4 and 5

Key themes

The following pages describe in detail activities related to three key themes for this age group:

Themes	Content boxes	
Growing and changing	(12)→(7)→(8)→(23)	(see page 31)
Keeping safe	(10)→(19)→(22)	(see page 41)
Medicine (drugs) and getting better	(2)→(3)→(25)	(see page 47)

It is important that you select and modify these activities according to your needs. If you are devising your own health education programme you may be well aware of the health education priorities of your school, and may have selected the key themes you wish to explore with your pupils. If this is the case, you may find that the following activities are useful examples. On the other hand, you may wish to incorporate them as they stand in your programme.

All the themes are explored through the content boxes which act as starting points for the activities. There are three other key themes relevant to this age group for which you may wish to plan your own activities:

Photocopy

4 & 5

Me & my relationships

12
Who are the people I meet each day? How do they know I am me? How do they recognise me? How do I recognise them?

13
Who are *my* special people? What do I do to make my special people happy? sad? worried? upset? angry?

14
What makes me feel good? extra good? special? better? Who makes me feel like that? How can I help to take care of the things and places special to me?

15
When do *I* feel happy or sad? worried? angry? hurt? loving? loved? lost? lonely? How does it feel to have friends? to quarrel? to be left behind? How does it feel when people or pets die?

16
How do healthy people look and feel? How do *I* look and feel when I am healthy?

17
How do not so healthy people look? What do they do? say? feel? How do I look when I am not so healthy? What do I do? say? feel?

18
What can I do when I am frightened? lost? bullied? upset? Who can help me?

19
How do I know which people, places, happenings, friends and pets are real or pretend? Is 'pretend' OK?

20
Good secrets and bad secrets. When should I tell? What do I say? Secret places and happenings: when are they safe? When are they dangerous? How can I say 'No' to people?

What are the words I need to know:

– to talk about feelings?

– to describe feeling good, safe and healthy?

– to describe feeling not so good, afraid, worried and lonely?

– to name family and friends?

– to talk about secrets?

– to get people to listen?

– to talk about real and pretend?

4 & 5

Me & my community & environment

21

Who are the people outside the home, with the special job of keeping me and places healthy and safe? For example, doctors, nurses, council workers, safety organisations.

22

Who are the people who keep me safe? What do they *do* to keep me safe? How do I help them? What do they do to make me *feel* safe? What makes me feel not so safe? upset? scared?

23

How do the people out there know I'm growing? What new things can I do? How do I recognise the people out there?

24

How do I know I am growing up? What places can I go to on my own? What new things are there to do? What new people are there to recognise? How do I recognise the people out there? What do they say? do? mean? How did the people out there help me grow up? What landmarks do I remember, for example, the clinic, the playgroup, swimming?

25

Who and what helps me to get better when I'm ill? Where do the people, and the medicines, come from to make me better? Where do we go to find them? Why must we be careful with medicines?

26

Where do I live? Where do you live? Where do we meet? For example, in school, on playgrounds, in shops, on the street, in church, Sunday school, in other people's homes.

27

Which places around here can we go to? Where are they? Who helps to keep them safe and clean? Which places aren't safe, clean or healthy? What can I do about it?

28

What can I see changing and growing all around here? What is new? old? alive? dead? dying? being born? Where do new things come from? For example, babies, plants, pets. Who are the new people in the class? in the home? in the family?

What are the words I need to know:

- to name the people out there?

- to name places out there?

- to describe clean and dirty?

- to describe growing and changing?

- to describe birth and death?

- to describe safe and dangerous?

- to talk about choosing, deciding and saying 'No'?

- to ask for help?

Themes	Content boxes
Looking at different lifestyles (including healthy eating, exercise, and personal hygiene)	
Family life and feelings	
Reality and fantasy	

(A summary of the main strategies and activities used in this chapter can be found on page 172).

Themes ● *Growing and changing*

Use content boxes 12, 7, 8 and 23:

12

Who are the people I meet each day? How do they know I am me? How do they recognise me? How do I recognise them?

7

How do I know I am growing? What can I reach? What can I do now? Which parts of me are growing? What size and shape are people? What size and shape am I? For example, small, middle-sized, tall.

23

How do the people out there know I am growing? What new things can I do? How do I recognise the people out there?

8

What do I think made me grow? Who helped me to grow?

This theme provides opportunities to explore early ideas of

- other people's lifestyles.
- body growth and change.
- growing up and growing responsibility.

Growing and changing

 Who are the people I meet each day? How do they know I am me? How do they recognise me? How do I recognise them?

Activity 1 ● *Me and the people around me*

- Talking together. Making a wall story or class book. Drawing, writing, and classroom play.

- Group or class activities, with opportunities for individual work.

Talk with the children about the people they see every day, or most days, at home, at school, or on the way to and from school.

How do the children recognise these people? What do these people do, wear and say? Do they wear special clothes? Where do the children see them? Can they imitate their actions and repeat some of what they hear them do and say?

Draw a large figure representing a child. Using the children's responses, write the names of the people they see around the figure and illustrate them (pin men will do).

Ask the children to decide which of these people they see at home, at school, and on the way to and from school.

Invite the children to think about what these people will be doing during the day, while they themselves are at school. In this way they will start to explore other people's lifestyles and see similarities and differences.

These are the people we have seen today

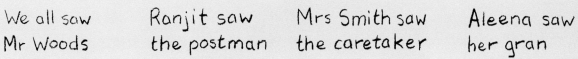

| We all saw Mr Woods | Ranjit saw the postman | Mrs Smith saw the caretaker | Aleena saw her gran |

Activity 2 ● *How do I know I'm me?*

- Talking together. Drawing and writing.
- Group and individual activities.

Children delight in trying to explain how people recognise them, and how their friends and families describe them.

Opportunities will arise to talk about:

− names and pet names.

− size.

− shape.

− colour of hair, eyes, skin and clothing.

This could be developed into an individual activity in which children draw themselves and (using the teacher as writer where appropriate) write about how people recognise them.

Who is it?

It's me Rob
my big hat

my big smile

my big boots

The children could also describe how specific people might recognise them, for example,

– the lollipop person
– the caretaker
– grandma

There are **cross-curricular links** with

– visitors to the classroom.
– visits – to watch some of these people at work.
– stories, poems, rhymes and jingles.

This aspect of lifestyles can be explored and extended in classroom play.

Growing and changing

7 **How do I know I am growing? What can I reach? What can I do now? Which parts of me are growing? What size and shape are people? What size and shape am I? For example, small, middle-sized, tall.**

Activity I ● *How do I know I'm growing?*

- Talking together. Drawing and writing. Making wall-stories and displays.
- Class or group activities, with opportunities for individual work.

Talk with the children about babies. Do the children recall being three years old? Two years old? One year old? Being a baby?

Talk about baby clothes and how small they are. Talk about what the children could and couldn't do when they were babies.

When I was a baby I couldn't:

walk   talk   climb

get dressed   read

go to school help my mum

feed myself

When I was a baby I could only

cry

feed from a bottle

crawl

Make a note of the children's responses. Invite them to sort through a collection of pictures cut from magazines to find pictures of babies, toddlers and school children. Make these into a display.

Invite the children to think about how they *know* they are growing. Ask them questions such as 'What are you able to *reach* now?' In what other ways do they know they are growing?

There are **cross-curricular links** with the vocabulary of size, for example, tall, small, taller, smaller, big, bigger, high, higher, highest, wider, larger.

It might be possible to ask a friend of the school to bring in a baby or toddler to help the children in making comparisons.

Activity 2 ● *Which parts of me are growing?*

- Talking together and drawing. Making a large picture or wall story.
- Class, small group and individual activities.

Talk with the children about how the different parts of their bodies have grown. How do they know that this growth has happened? Write down and display the children's ideas and illustrate them, or ask them to contribute to the illustrations.

Read and reread this display with the children. Encourage them to make individual versions to take away and add to at home.

Activity 3 ● *What size and shape am I?*

- ● Talking together. Drawing and painting.

- ● Class, group and individual activities.

Talk with the children about the different sizes and shapes people have (you will need to be sensitive to children's feelings about their own size and shape).

Extend their vocabulary of size and shape: tall, small, middle-sized, big, bigger, biggest, thin, not so thin, long legs, long arms.

Ask the children to paint pictures of different people, pets, flowers and trees etc. on the theme 'People are all different sizes and shapes'. Label them with this kind of vocabulary. Draw around children, cut out the figure shapes and group according to different criteria.

There are **cross-curricular links** with

- — PE: size and shape can be explored in physical activities such as reaching and stretching up.

- — mathematical language: sorting and grouping activities can be introduced or reinforced.

- — science: skills such as observation can be introduced.

Growing and changing

8 **What do I think made me grow? Who helped me to grow?**

Activity 1 ● *What made me grow? Who helped me to grow?*

- Talking together. Drawing and contributing to a shared picture or display.

- Class or group activities with opportunities for individual work, writing through the teacher, and painting.

Talk with the children about how much they have grown. Invite them to draw and label pictures of people and all the things that helped them to grow. (You can write for them.)

Look at the children's responses and make a note of the most frequent, the most unusual and the most unexpected responses.

Use the children's responses to make up a large shared picture, or to make up a rhyme or jingle to read and reread.

Use the theme of growth as the starting point for painting and picture-making, on the theme of portraits.

There are **cross-curricular links** with stories, poems, rhymes and songs.

Growing and changing

23 **How do the people out there know I am growing? What new things can I do? How do I recognise the people out there?**

Activity 1 ● ***Now I am growing – where do I go?***

- Talking together. Classroom play, drawing and writing.

- Working in groups or pairs with the opportunity for individual activity.

Talk with the children about some of the places they go to now they are growing up. (This is an opportunity for some relevant safety education.) Who takes them? Do they ever go alone? Do they want to go? Do they *have* to go? You could plan to visit some of these places.

Encourage the children to explore what happens when they go to these places using classroom play. What do people say at these places? Do these places have a special vocabulary of their own?

Invite the children to write about both the play and the visits they make.

We have been playing
going to the library

Joanie was the library
lady

She said

Take care of
the books

Philo stamped
the books

Sonia put the
books away

Now I am growing up

I go to the
dentist
with my
dad

I had to
get new
shoes

I go to the
big church

I go to
the big
pool

Activity 2 ● *Now I am growing up, what can I do?*

- Talking together. Sorting and grouping pictures. Drawing and writing.
- Class, group, and individual activities.

I can clean my own teeth

I can choose my drink

I can read a book

I can put my shoes and coat on

Talk with the children about the things they can now do for themselves. Ask them to draw and write about the things they can do and help you to make a shared chart.

Provide the children with a collection of cut-out pictures. Include pictures of people of all ages, from a variety of lifestyles, doing a variety of activities. Ask the children to sort these into sets, using the criteria:

- Things I can do *now*.
- Things I will be able to do *soon*.
- Things I can't do *yet*.
- Things I want to do.

Ask the children to talk you through their sorting procedure. Talk about the things they want to be able to do. Can they start to learn some of the skills (or see the risks) involved?

There are **cross-curricular links** with

- classroom play.
- visits and visitors.
- stories, poems and rhymes.
- art.

Theme ● *Keeping safe*

Use content boxes 10, 19 and 22:

What do I think I have to keep safe from? How do I think I do this? What real and pretend things should I keep safe from?

→

How do I know which people, places, happenings, friends and pets are real or pretend? Is pretend OK?

→

Who are the people who keep me safe? What do they *do* to keep me safe? How do I help them? What do they do to make me *feel* safe? What makes me feel not so safe? upset? scared?

This theme provides opportunities to explore:

- home, road and water safety.
- imaginary fears.
- bullying.
- aspects of child abuse.

Keeping safe

10 What do I think I have to keep safe from? How do I think I do this? What real and pretend things should I keep safe from?

Activity I ● *What do I think I have to keep safe from?*

- Talking together. Drawing and writing.

- Group or class activity with opportunities for individual work.

Explore the children's perceptions of what they think they have to keep safe from by inviting them to draw pictures of themselves keeping safe, and pictures of things they are keeping safe from. Invite the children to share what they have drawn. Help them to label their drawings, particularly what they see as hazards and dangers.

Talk with the children about the real and imaginary hazards which are found indoors and outdoors.

Display some of their drawings and dictated writing.

This is our class keeping ourselves safe

Encourage the children to talk about how they keep themselves safe from the hazards they have identified. Their answers are likely to focus on 'don'ts', for example, 'Don't touch', 'Don't go out', 'Don't let them in', 'Don't run'; or, 'Hide', 'Run away', 'Hold on', 'Go and watch TV'. Encourage them to extend these ideas by talking about the importance of:

– staying with the known;

– not wandering off, going off with older children or unknown people;

– not touching, or tasting;

– saying 'No', 'I don't want to', 'Please help me';

– learning that different places have different rules.

Ask them to practice 'telling': describing places, people and feelings.

Cross-curricular links: classroom play, movement, drama and PE can all be used to reinforce these themes.

Keeping safe

19 **How do I know which people, places, happenings, friends and pets are real or pretend? Is 'pretend' OK?**

Activity 1 ● *Real and pretend people, places and happenings*

- Use children's literature, stories, poems and rhymes, as a basis for discussion. Make a wall story incorporating the children's drawings and writing.

- Class and group activities with opportunities for individual work.

Literature can provide a starting point for children to talk about real or imaginary characters, and happenings; about toys which sometimes have a life of their own; about imaginary friends and pets. Television programmes will also provide starting points for talk.

Invite the children to draw and label some of the real, and some of the imaginary, characters and happenings they have encountered.

Collect their observations, illustrations, and writing and make a wall story for reading, rereading and adding to. It could be interesting and useful to invite members of the children's families to come and share the wall story.

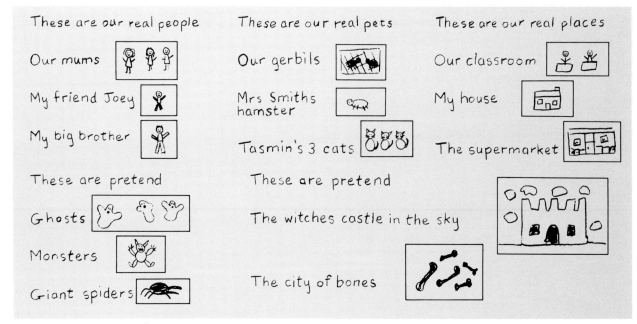

Without discouraging children from having imaginary worlds, it is important for their safety that they learn to differentiate between reality and fantasy. You will need to take into account the impact of television on children, as by its very nature, it makes it difficult for them to distinguish between what is real and what is fantasy.

Keeping safe

 Who are the people who keep me safe? What do they *do* to keep me safe? How do I help them? What do they do to make me *feel* safe? What makes me feel not so safe? upset? scared?

Activity 1 ● *The people who keep me safe*

- Talking together. Classroom play, painting, and collage making.

- Group and class activity, with opportunities for shared and individual activities.

Invite the children to think about all the people who help to keep them safe throughout the day. Explore this in movement and classroom play: work through the children's day, starting with getting up in the morning.

Briefly illustrate (pin people will do) the list of people and places which are part of the children's day, for example,

- in my house
- on the way to school
- at school
- out of school
- my family

- crossing patrol
- teacher, caretaker, school nurse
- other adults, friends, and religious figures, police, park and pool attendants, fire brigade, ambulance people

Ask the children to paint large pictures of the people who help to keep them safe:

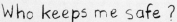

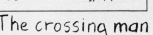

Activity 2 ● *What do I do to help?*

- Talking together about the children's own role in keeping themselves safe.

- Class or group activity.

Reread with the children the wall story they have made in Activity 1: 'People who keep me safe'.

Look at each character in turn. Invite the children to say or act out ways in which they could make the character happy by helping them, and ways in which they might make the character sad, worried or angry by not helping them.

Follow up this activity by inviting the children to draw themselves being helpful (or not so helpful) with labels or explanations.

Activity 3 ● *How do they make me feel safe?*

- Talking together.
- Small group activities.

Talk with the children about what these helpful people do or say to make people feel safe. Young children are often very aware of this aspect of safety and can be encouraged to put their thoughts into words. Classroom play often provides the key.

This could be the time to introduce small group talk about people who do not make us feel safe, such as bullies, people who tease, push smaller people about or touch our bodies in ways which upset or threaten us. If classroom play and role-play have been well established, this could be a good time to explore the skills of moving away, of telling an adult, and of saying 'No'.

This is a good time to use stories about conquering or reducing fear, dealing with threats and with real and imaginary fears and dangers.

You can involve visits or visitors and invite family co-operation and reinforcement. For example, you could ask parents to encourage the children to explain what they have been doing in school when they take home their drawing and writing.

Theme *Medicines (drugs) and getting better*

Use content boxes 2, 3 and 25:

2

What goes *onto* my body? Who puts it there? For example, soap, water, shampoo, dirt, paint, ointment, plasters, sun, air, clothing, shoes.

→

3

What goes *into* my body? Who puts it there? For example, food, drink, medicine, pills, air, dust, smoke, smells. How does it get in? How does it make me feel? Where do I think it goes?

→

25

Who and what helps me to get better when I'm ill? Where do the people, and the medicines, come from to make me better? Where do we go to find them? Why must we be careful with medicines?

This theme provides opportunities to explore:

- the hazards and dangers of medicines, pills and other substances.
- the role of health professionals.
- the basic rules of hygiene and the earliest notions of germs invading the body.

Medicines (drugs) and getting better

2 **What goes *onto* my body? Who puts it there? For example, soap, water, shampoo, dirt, paint, ointment, plasters, sun, air, clothing, shoes.**

Activity 1   ●   *What goes onto my body?*

- Talking together, and using the children's responses to make a wall story. This can be added to later and used for revision.

- Class or group activity.

Ask the children what they put onto their bodies when they get up in the morning. Their first responses may focus on clothing so invite them to think of other situations, for example, getting washed.

Encourage them to talk about other times of the day. What else do they put onto their bodies? When they are out playing? When they are having their hair washed? When they have a sore or a cut?

Draw a large figure of a child or actually draw round a child in the class. Around the figure, stick on, or draw, pictures of the things children think go onto their bodies and label them. Both you and the children can do the drawing and writing as you talk. Read through the work as you go. Read and reread the wall story.

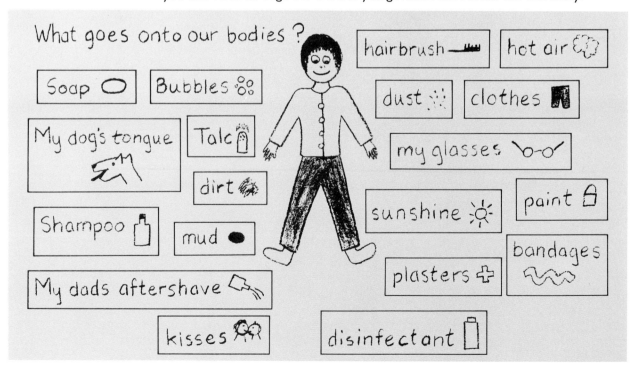

Talk with the children about how they feel when they (or someone else) puts these different things onto their bodies. Which of these things feel good, and not so good? Which of these things please adults? Which of them make adults cross? Why?

Ask the children to pick out any of these situations which might be dangerous and encourage them to say why. (It is important to discover the children's explanations before you talk with them about sensitive issues.)

Activity 2 ● ***Who puts it there?***

- Talking together.
- Class or small group activity.

Return to the wall chart 'What goes onto our bodies?'

Reread the captions with the children asking each time 'Who puts it there?' The children will have differing and interesting answers, especially relating to air, dust and sun. Ask them, in each case, to explain: 'What happens to it?' 'Does it disappear?', 'Does someone take it off? If so – who?'

Family work: some children could make their own versions of the wall chart, either using a worksheet or devising their own format. The children could take these home and explain them to their families and invite them to make additions.

Medicines (drugs) and getting better

3 **What goes *into* my body? Who puts it there? For example, food, drink, medicine, pills, air, dust, smoke, smells. How does it get in? How does it make me feel? Where do I think it goes?**

Activity 1 ● *What goes into my body?*

The strategies and activities suggested for content box 2, 'What goes *onto* my body?' can be used again but with a change of focus.

Encourage children to think of all the ways in which 'things' can enter their bodies, for example, by breathing, eating, drinking and sniffing; via mouth, ears and eyes; by injection or by accident, for example, splinters, wasp stings, nails, pins or thorns. Encourage them to think widely, to include medicines, pills, berries, smoke, fumes, pleasant smells and scents.

Talk with the children about their feelings when different things enter their bodies, such as delight, pain or fear. Invite them to talk about who puts these things into them, and to identify those which are dangerous, those which they should only do with adult permission and supervision, and those which they should never do. Encourage them to explain why they believe certain things could be dangerous and what the outcomes might be. It may be possible at this stage to talk about dirt and germs getting into their bodies and the importance of personal hygiene.

It is important at this stage to discover as much as possible about the children's perceptions of what is inside them, before planning any teaching about the dangers of specific substances.

Activity 2 ● *Where do I think it all goes?*

● Painting and drawing.

● Individual or small group work.

Invite the children to paint large scale pictures of what they think is inside their bodies. Display the pictures and talk with the children about what happens when all the different things they have talked about enter their bodies. Where does food and drink go? Pills? Injections? The children's unprompted perceptions of the bloodstream and digestion will be most revealing.

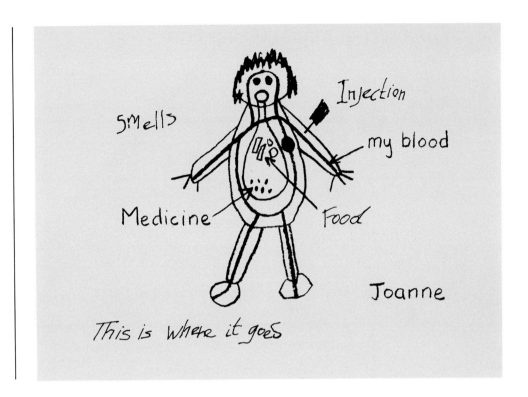

Smells

Injection

my blood

Medicine

Food

Joanne

This is where it goes

Most children will not be ready for formal descriptions, diagrams and language for parts of the body. The analysis of their perceptions and explanations will enable you to plan your teaching.

Medicines (drugs) and getting better

25 Who and what helps me to get better when I'm ill? Where do the people, and the medicines, come from to make me better? Where do we go to find them? Why must we be careful with medicines?

Activity 1 ● *Who helps me to get better when I'm ill?*

- Talking and using classroom play. Recording children's responses as a wall story or class book. Drawing and painting in different media.

- Class, group and individual activities.

Invite the children to share what it is like to be ill, in talk, mime or classroom play. How did they look? What hurt? What itched? What did they have to do or not do? Did they have to take any medicine? With the children, note down their responses as a piece of shared writing.

Invite the children to write their own accounts of what it is like to be ill and illustrate them. Display these around the shared writing.

Activity 2 ● *Where did the people come from to make me better?*

- Talking together and sharing experiences.

- Class or group activity.

Reread both the shared writing, and the children's individual accounts from Activity 1.

Ask the children what and who make them better. Write down their responses and read and reread them.

Ask the children if they can say where all these people and things came from. Keep them to write about and illustrate this.

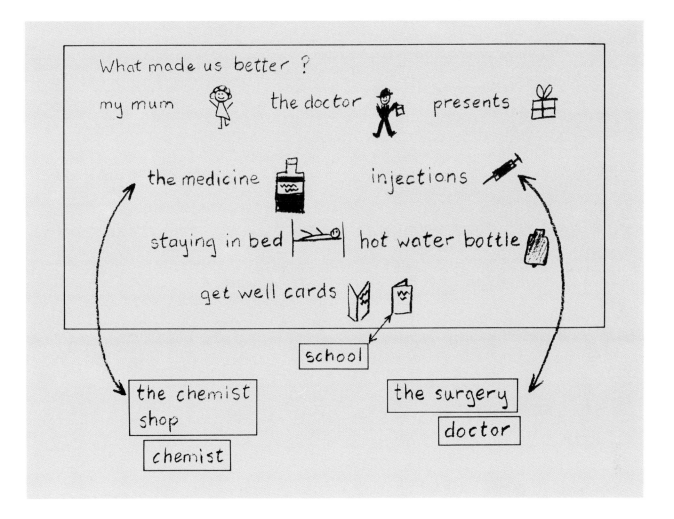

There are opportunities here to talk about the caring aspect of getting better, as well as to look at where medicines and pills come from, and the early safety rules, for example, children should:

– only take medicines when they are given them by a doctor, nurse, parent or responsible adult.

– never swallow anything they find in bottles, jars or packs of pills.

Activity 3 ● *Keeping safe with medicines*

● Make and use a collage of a cupboard (bathroom or kitchen) as a starting point for talking about and practising medicine safety rules.

● Class or small group activities.

Give the children cut-out or torn-out pictures from magazines depicting toothpaste, talc, soap, shampoo, cough medicine, tablets, creams, lotions, etc.

Stick these pictures onto an outline of an open cupboard with several shelves.

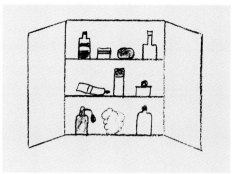

Invite the children to talk about the items and to identify and label those which are dangerous. Ask them to explain why. (This will enable you to see something of the logic they use and to gauge the impact of the previous activities on safety.)

Encourage the children to use the collage as a backdrop for a small scale play, using improvised paper figures or dolls. Help them to devise role-plays with good and not so good endings.

Family work: children could take home an individual version of this work to share with their families:

We have been learning about medicines and pills and keeping safe

We made a picture of a cupboard with lots of things in

We put ● by the dangerous ones

Can we look in our cupboard and see if there are any dangerous things?

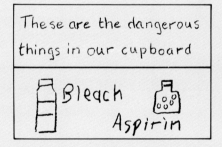

These are the dangerous things in our cupboard

Bleach Aspirin

There are **cross-curricular links** with visits into, and visitors from, the community.

Photocopy

6 & 7 Action planner
Me & looking after myself

1

My special body, my special face, my size, shape and colour. Are we the same? Are we different?

2

It's what I *do* to my body that makes and keeps it healthy. What do I do? What do I put *on* it and *in* it? Who tells me to do this?

3

What do I eat? What do I like to eat and drink? Why do I eat? What meals do people eat? When? Where? Who tells me what to eat and drink? When can I choose for myself? What helps me to choose? What helps me to stick to my choice or to change my mind? For example, TV, friends, learning about food.

4

How do I think my body is changing? How has it changed since I was a baby and since I came to school? What makes it change and grow?

5

Am I feeling good about my body? Am I enjoying what it can do? What can I make it do? How does this make me feel?

6

What do I do to look after myself each day? For example, personal hygiene, keeping safe, exercise, sleep, rest, play, work.

7

What do I think I do to make and keep myself healthy? What else do I need to know about being healthy? What is a healthy day for me?

8

What do I think is inside me? What is my skeleton like – and my heart? Where are the different systems in my body? How do I think they work?

9

How do I think healthy people look? feel? live? What is their message to us? What about not so healthy people? What is my message to them? What do healthy people do some of the time? all the time? never? What is a healthy day for them?

10

What do not so healthy people do some of the time? all the time? never? How do they look? feel? live? What is my message to them?

11

What happens to my body when I exercise? What can I see happening? What do I think happens inside me when I exercise?

12

What do I think I have to keep safe from – at home? at school? outside? How do I think I keep safe?

13

What happens when I sleep and rest? What happens when I am ill? What happens when I am given medicine and injections? What can I do – or not do – to get better?

What are the words I need to know:

– to describe formally parts of the body? (What are *my* words?)

– to describe how these parts work?

Classroom strategies and activities for ages 6 and 7

● **Key themes**

The following pages describe in detail activities related to three key themes for this age group:

Themes	Content boxes
Healthy lifestyles (including exercise, rest, and personal hygiene)	⑨→⑦→㉖ (see page 59)
Healthy eating	③→㉞→㉓ (see page 68)
Feelings and relationships (including family life and personal safety)	⑭→⑳→㊱ (see page 76)

It is important that you select and modify these activities according to your needs. If you are devising your own health education programme you may be well aware of the health education priorities of your school, and may have selected the key themes you wish to explore with your pupils. If this is the case, you may find that the following activities are useful examples. On the other hand, you may wish to incorporate them as they stand in your programme.

All the themes are explored through the content boxes which act as starting points for the activities. There are three other key themes relevant to this age group for which you may wish to plan your own activities:

Me & my relationships

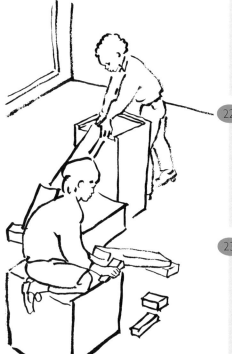

14
What makes me the same as you? What are the feelings we all share? For example, being happy, sad, cheerful, afraid, uneasy, shy, clumsy. What makes us different? How does it feel to be different?

15
What do we all (children and grown-ups) do? For example, love, quarrel, lose friends, pets, treasures; grow, grow up, grow older; work, play, get tired.

16
How does it feel to be like other people? How does it feel to be different?

17
How do you know I am me? How do you know how I feel? What tells you: my face? my body language? my voice? What can you do to understand how I feel? For example, listen, look, hug, and help.

18
Who are my special people? Who are your special people? What do they do for me? say to me? tell me? How do I show them they are special? How do they show me I am special?

19
What do I do to make my special people happy? happier? worried? angry? better? What do they do to make me feel happy? worried? angry? better?

20
What makes me feel good about myself and my days? How do I feel when I feel good? What can I do to help make myself feel good?

21
What can I do when I am frightened? lost? bullied? upset? What can I learn to do? How can I say 'No', 'Yes', 'I can't', 'I won't', 'I don't' and 'Stop'?

22
How does it feel when special people or things change, leave or are lost or die? Who can help me to understand? What can they do?

23
What makes some of my days special? For example, good experiences, happenings, surprises and food. What are the days I remember and the days I look forward to? For example happy times, sad times, landmarks.

24
What makes other people's days better or special? Getting on with other people: how can I make their days special? For example, by listening, visiting and caring.

25
How does it feel when I've done something new or difficult? helped someone? mastered a problem? enjoyed something?

What are the words I need to know:

– to tell people how I feel?

– to describe how other people feel?

– to tell people I feel confident?

– to describe being special and valued?

– to describe how other people are special?

6 & 7 Me & my community & environment

26
What do I think makes places healthy or not so healthy?

27
How do I think I keep myself safe? Whose job is it to keep me safe? What's my part of this job?

28
Where do I live? Where do you live? Who else lives here? there? nearby? How are we all the same? How are we different? What do other people do? Where do they all meet? For example, the street, shops, pubs, clubs, church. Where do I meet them?

29
Who looks after me and my health and safety? Where do they work? Can we go and see? Whose job is it to keep me healthy and safe? Is it my job too? How do I recognise (and trust) these people? For example, I go by what they wear and say and by what they tell me to do. Do I feel good, or not so good, about what they do?

30
Who keeps safe the places that I go to? What is their message to us? How can I help?

31
How do I know I am growing up? Where can I go now on my own? with friends? with other grown-ups? Can I decide for myself? Who and when must I ask?

32
Special occasions at school, home and in the neighbourhood, for me and for others: meetings, parades, fetes, carnivals, celebrations. What makes them special for me? for you? for others?

33
What can I do to help the people who have few or no special times?

34
Who keeps food clean and safe? What can I do to help?

35
What makes some places special? Why are quiet places special? noisy and crowded places? places for being alone? places for sharing? secret places? real and imaginary places? What are safe places for dangerous things? For example, medicine cabinets, cupboards, handbags, shops and sheds. What dangerous things can I see, reach and touch?

36
Who are our special people and friends? What do they do and say? What do we do together? What do we share or keep secret? What do I like about them, and like doing with them? What makes me scared sometimes or uneasy? Whom can I tell?

37
What do I think makes things, places and people safe or not so safe?

What are the words I need to know:

— to name people and their jobs?

— to describe being sure and not so sure?

— to talk about danger and dangerous objects?

— to ask for help and instruction?

Themes	Content boxes
Keeping safe*	(12)→(27)→(29)
How my body works, grows and changes	(4)→(8)→(11)→(5)
The world of medicines and drugs*	(2)→(13)→(29)→(35)

(A summary of the main strategies and activities used in this chapter can be found on page 172).

(*Additional material provided in *Health for Life 2*, see Appendix 2, page 186).

Theme ● *Healthy lifestyles*

Use content boxes 9, 7 and 26:

9

How do I think healthy people look? feel? live? What is their message to us? What about not so healthy people? What is my message to them? What do healthy people do some of the time? all the time? never? What is a healthy day for them?

→

7

What do I think I do to make and keep myself healthy? What else do I need to know about being healthy? What is a healthy day for me?

→

26

What do I think makes places healthy or not so healthy?

This theme provides opportunities for:

- extending children's understanding of their own and others' healthy lifestyles.
- starting to develop an evaluation framework for describing lifestyles as healthy or not so healthy.

Healthy lifestyles

9 How do I think healthy people look? feel? live? What is their message to us? What about not so healthy people? What is my message to them? What do healthy people do some of the time? all the time? never? What is a healthy day for them?

Activity 1 ● *How do healthy people look?*

- Painting pictures of healthy and not so healthy people.

- Shared or individual activities.

Invite the children to show, with facial expressions, and body posture and movements, how healthy people feel, look and move. Contrast this with how not so healthy people look, feel and move. Invite the children to paint large scale pictures of healthy and not so healthy people and to explain to others how these people look and how healthy and not so healthy characteristics are portrayed.

Ask the children to help make decisions about displaying the pictures. Should all the pictures of healthy people be grouped together, or should pictures be displayed in pairs showing one healthy and one not so healthy person?

Activity 2 ● *What is their message?*

- Language activity, focusing on what healthy and not so healthy people might be saying.

- Small group shared activity, followed by individual activities.

Provide some large cut-out speech and thought bubbles. Look again at the display of pictures from Activity 1. Invite the children to empathise with the characters they have painted. Can they make themselves look like these characters and try to feel as they might feel?

What might the characters be saying? Involve the children in deciding on the messages to write in the speech and thought bubbles.

Read and reread the messages together, experimenting with different kinds of voices.

What kind of message do the children have for the not so healthy characters? Make a note of some of their ideas. Invite each child to draw herself or himself and write (or dictate) a message for the not so healthy characters.

Activity 3 ● *What do healthy people do?*

- Shared discussion with the children pooling and sorting their ideas.

- Small group or class activity.

Return to the children's paintings of healthy and not so healthy people, and to the messages the children helped to write.

Invite the children to talk about what they think healthy people do and don't do. Note their answers. It is likely that these will focus on eating, drinking, taking exercise, dental care and fresh air. Encourage the children to think back to how healthy people *feel* (explored in Activity 1), to maintain their holistic view of healthy lifestyles.

Ask the children if they can help to sort the activities they have suggested. Possible categories might be: eating and drinking, exercise, sleep, 'don'ts', keeping clean, teeth, fresh air, getting on with people, being happy.

The children could illustrate some of these activities and put their pictures into the different 'boxes' on a wall chart.

What do healthy people do ?		
Eating 🍎 Drinking	Exercise	Sleep
Don'ts	keeping clean	Teeth
Fresh air	Getting on with people	Being happy

Return to what the children have contributed, to talk about which of the activities healthy people do

— all the time,

— some of the time,

— never.

This will provide opportunities to explore notions of 'every day', 'twice a day', 'regularly' and 'occasionally'.

Invite the children to contribute to a list beginning 'Healthy people don't . . .', and to give their explanations of *why* they don't. This will reveal much of the way children think and what they know, and will provide you with starting points for introducing new learning.

Activity 4 ● ***Healthy messages***

- Revision, leading to inventing 'healthy messages'.
- Class or group activity.

Revise all the work relating to content box 9, rereading the children's displayed drawing, painting and writing.

Make, or draw, a Healthy Message Board. Recall the activities of healthy people, their healthy days and their messages. Invite the children to write and illustrate healthy messages to go on the board. Some ready made banners and flags would be useful.

Family work: suggest to the children that they take home one of the message banners to fill in with the help of the family and display these at home or at school.

Activity 5 ● *What is a healthy day?*

- Talking together, sorting cut-out pictures and grouping them into healthy activities which could be part of a healthy day.

- Small group activity.

Start a collection of cut-out pictures from magazines of people engaged in all types of healthy activity. They should illustrate: hygiene, exercise, food, caring for others, the environment, keeping safe, being happy, resting, sleeping and relaxing.

Invite pairs or small groups of children to look through the pictures and arrange them to show a healthy day. Talk with the children about what they have included.

There are **cross-curricular links** with teaching the language of

– times of day, and

– telling the time.

Healthy lifestyles

7 **What do I think I do to make and keep myself healthy? What else do I need to know about being healthy? What is a healthy day for me?**

Activity 1 ● *What do I think I do to make and keep myself healthy?*

- Finding out more about the children's explanations of keeping healthy.
- Class or group activity with individual starting points.

This would be a good time to use the investigation technique (see Appendix 1, page 176) which asks children to draw and label all those things they do, or think they do, to make and keep themselves healthy.

You could analyse the responses, inviting the children to help, setting out the results pictorially.

Exercise | Food | Cleaning teeth | Fresh air | Playing with friends | My family | Washing

Mrs Jones wanted to know what we did to make us healthy and keep us healthy. She wouldn't let us talk first. It was a secret game. Now you can see what we said.

Activity 2 ● *What else do I need to know?*

- Talking together, exploring the children's perceptions and explanations of how exercise, food, fresh air, etc. keep people healthy.
- Group and individual activities.

Some children may be ready to explore the ways in which their bodies work in a more scientific way, others will be ready to explore relationships more fully. Using a 'Finding Out Board' and special collections of books can motivate these new moves and provide opportunities for extending early study skills.

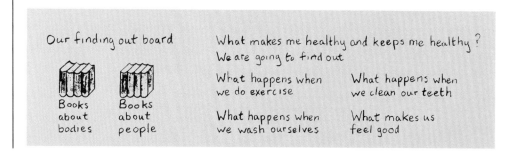

Our finding out board

Books about bodies | Books about people

What makes me healthy and keeps me healthy? We are going to find out

What happens when we do exercise

What happens when we clean our teeth

What happens when we wash ourselves

What makes us feel good

Activity 3 ● *What is a healthy day for me?*

- Talking together.

- Class, group or individual activities.

Invite the children to talk about their days, looking at what they do to make and keep themselves healthy. Look at similarities and differences. There are opportunities here to learn about each other's lifestyles.

Ask the children to illustrate and label, or write about, different aspects of their healthy days.

There are **cross-curricular links** with:

— understanding time and

— telling the time.

> Healthy day words
>
> in the morning   in PE
>
> at playtime   when I get home
>
> before school   I choose
>
> at dinner time   I clean I help

Activity 4 ● *How healthy is my day?*

- Evaluating lifestyles.

- Class, group and individual activity, with opportunities for family work.

Revise the previous work on healthy activities and healthy days.

Provide the children with a framework to fill in (see illustration), or ask them to prepare it for themselves. Talk through each of the following three steps with the children:

— This is me keeping healthy.

— This is what I need to do more often.

— This is what I need to do less.

Ask the children to complete each step with both drawing and writing.

This might be an opportunity for a group to devise a simple contract and to involve home and family.

Contract

I am going to try ....

I am going to ask ....

.... to help me.

Signed ....

Healthy lifestyles

26 **What do I think makes places healthy or not so healthy?**

Activity 1 ● *What makes places healthy or not so healthy?*

- Talking together. Making a wall story.

- Class or group activity.

Invite the children to think whether places like people, can be healthy. How does a healthy place look? For example, a school.

A healthy school

is

clean, not smelly
warm, cool, happy
has nice dinners
soap in the toilet
good lessons
lots of PE   no bullies
nice people, places to play
someone to make you better
you can stay in when its cold
nobody smokes

Make a note of the children's responses and use them to make a wall story listing the characteristics of a healthy school. What do the responses focus on? Encourage children to explain:

– how these characteristics make a school healthy,

– how much the happiness of a school matters to its health.

Talk about whose job it is to make and keep the school healthy. How can the children themselves make the job easier or harder?

These characteristics could be used by the children to look at their own classroom, school building and playground in a different way and to decide what they themselves could do to help or improve things.

There are **cross-curricular links** with

– topic work (especially on the environment or 'People who care for us').

– visits and visitors.

– role-playing.

– home and family.

Theme ● *Healthy eating*

Use content boxes 3, 34 and 23:

3

What do I eat? What do I like to eat and drink? Why do I eat? What meals do people eat? When? Where? Who tells me what to eat and drink? When can I choose? What helps me to choose? What helps me to stick to my choice or to change my mind? For example, TV, friends, learning about food.

→

34

Who keeps food clean and safe? What can I do to help?

→

23

What makes some of my days special? For example, good experiences, happenings, surprises and food. What are the days I remember and the days I look forward to? For example, happy times, sad times, landmarks.

This theme provides opportunities for extending children's

- views on healthy eating.
- understanding of the relationship between healthy eating and their own and other people's lifestyles.
- understanding of other people's lifestyles.

Healthy eating

3 What do I eat? What do I like to eat and drink? Why do I eat? What meals do people eat? When? Where? Who tells me what to eat and drink? When can I choose? What helps me to choose? What helps me to stick to my choice or to change my mind? For example, friends, TV, learning about food.

Activity 1 ● *What healthy eating means to me*

- Talking together. Sharing ideas and explanations. Drawing, labelling and analysing.

- Class, group and individual activities.

Invite the children to draw a picture of themselves feeling hungry. Collect words which describe the feeling of hunger, for example, 'pain in the tummy', 'weak', 'grumpy'.

Ask the children to draw and label the foods and drinks they think keep them healthy. Ask them to help you present their views as a chart (see illustration) which shows the number of times each food is mentioned in their work.

Which foods and drinks make us healthy?			
fruit	vegetables	milk	eggs/cheese
✓ ✓ ✓ ✓ ✓ ✓ ✓ ✓ ✓ ✓	✓ ✓ ✓ ✓ ✓ ✓ ✓ ✓ ✓ ✓ ✓ ✓	✓ ✓ ✓ ✓	✓ ✓ ✓ ✓ ✓ ✓
10 of us said fruit	12 of us said vegetables	4 of us said milk	6 of us said eggs or cheese

Explore with the children what they think it is *about* these foods or *in* these foods that makes them healthy. It is important to discover how children explain this before starting to provide them with new information. Many children may respond in a general way with 'it's good things in them' and this can provide a starting point for teaching. It is wise to avoid the use of labels such as 'foods which are good for us' or 'foods which are bad for us' and to distinguish between 'health foods' and healthy foods.

Activity 2 ● *Why do I eat and what do I eat?*

- Class or group activity: talking together and pooling ideas, or,

- individual activity: asking the children to explain in drawing and writing why they eat, and to share their ideas.

Children's own explanations of why they eat are very illuminating and provide starting points for the wider exploration of the physical and social aspects of food.

With the children make a list of foods which they like. Talk with them about why they like these foods. You may get a range of answers like these:

- 'Because I like the taste . . .'

- '. . . they're grown-up . . .'

- '. . . they're special . . .'

- '. . . we go out to eat them . . .'

- '. . . my Mum likes them . . .'

Activities like these provide opportunities to talk about other people's foods and food traditions and to help the children become more aware of differences in lifestyles as well as differences in healthy lifestyles.

Activity 3 ● *When and where do we eat?*

- Exploring the children's and other people's eating habits. Making a wall story, collages and class or group books.

- Class or group activities with opportunities for individual and family work.

Ask the children to build up a list of names for the meals they eat throughout the day. Explore with the children the time of day and the occasions on which these meals are eaten.

How are sweets and ice creams referred to? For example, 'treats'.

Explore with the children where they eat and with whom. Ask them to tear or cut out pictures from magazines which illustrate this, and individually, or in groups, make them into collages.

Some groups could go on to explore who provides the food, who prepares it, who clears it away and who tells them to eat it.

Talk about the meaning of the word 'breakfast' and the importance of this meal after a night without food.

Family work: children could make their own books, incorporating all these ideas and take them home to share with their families, inviting them to make contributions.

Activity 4 ● *Choosing for myself*

- Talking together about who tells us what to eat and about choosing food for ourselves.

- Class or group activity.

Opportunities for children in this age range to choose for themselves may be limited, but children will recognise times when they can influence food choices.

Talk with the children about a meal they have eaten recently. Who told them to eat it? What did this person say?

Talk about times when the children think they have had some choice:

— at school

— at home

— in the shop

— in the café and take-away shop

— for packed lunch

Talk about choosing 'foods which make you healthy' in these situations. Ask them to look out for more opportunities to choose them.

There are opportunities to

— encourage a positive approach to healthy eating and introduce early ideas on limiting the fat, sugar and salt in our diets.

— encourage a greater awareness of other people's lifestyles, special occasions and celebrations.

— introduce early survey and pictorial representation skills.

— use classroom play, setting up 'shops' and cafés', exploring themes about buying, preparing and cooking food, sharing meals and celebrating.

— use home links and **family work**.

There are **cross-curricular links** with home economics.

Healthy eating

34 **Who keeps my food clean and safe? What can I do to help?**

Activity 1 ● *Where does my food come from?*

- Talking together. Making a diagram or map showing the sources of the food which the children eat.

- Group or class activity.

This is a useful starting point for exploring many aspects of healthy eating. Here it is used to help the children focus on food hygiene.

Invite the children to talk about where their food comes from, how it travels, and how many people handle it. Make a map or diagram to illustrate this, representing distance in some way, pin men will do.

Ask the children to suggest ways in which food can be made to stay fresh and clean, and reasons why it might spoil.

Focus on day-to-day aspects of food hygiene, particularly children washing their hands before handling food, after playing (especially with pets) and after using the lavatory.

There are opportunities to talk about flies and the spreading of disease.

There are **cross-curricular links** with:

– topic work.

– visits and visitors.

– creative activities such as painting and model-making (appropriate for exploring the sources of foods).

There are opportunities to begin looking at the lifestyles of a range of people involved in the production, transport and hygiene of food.

Healthy eating

23 What makes some of my days special? For example, good experiences, happenings, surprises and food. What are the days I remember and the days I look forward to? For example, happy times, sad times, landmarks.

Activity 1 ● *Our special days*

- Talking together, exploring the relationships between good and special occasions of many different kinds using writing, drawing and painting.

- Shared and individual activities with opportunities for family work.

Many special occasions, landmarks and memories are linked with food, and by exploring them you can teach children more about eating for health.

Talk with the children about a recent special occasion, either a shared one, or one in which only some of the children were involved. Ask them to describe the foods which were part of the occasion. Write down and read through the children's responses. This could be an opportunity to use role-play.

> Our special days
>
> Pancake Day
>
> Divali
>
> my friend coming to tea
>
> Ramadan
>
> New Year
>
> my birthday
>
> my great grans birthday
>
> school trips
>
> my friend's mums wedding

Invite the children as a group to describe the special nature of the preparation and eating of food on special occasions. Invite them to choose illustrations of food which have been drawn, painted, or cut from magazines, and to label or write about them.

Activity 2 ● *My special days*

- Making individual versions of the shared writing and drawing from Activity 1.
- Individual activity followed by sharing.

Talk with the group about different kinds of special days. Which ones can they remember? Include both good and not so good days. Was food part of the celebration? Was food comforting on a sad occasion?

There are **cross-curricular links** with:

- history, geography and literature.

- learning about other cultures and traditions.

- making visits and inviting visitors to the school.

- cooking and/or tasting a wide variety of foods eaten on special occasions.

Theme *Feelings and relationships*

Use content boxes 14, 20 and 36:

14

What makes me the same as you? What are the feelings we all share? For example, being happy, sad, cheerful, afraid, uneasy, shy, clumsy. What makes us different? How does it feel to be different? →

20

What makes me feel good about myself and my days? How do I feel when I feel good? What can I do to help make myself feel good? →

36

Who are our special people and friends? What do they do and say? What do we do together? What do we share or keep secret? What do I like about them, and like doing with them? What makes me scared sometimes or uneasy? Whom can I tell?

This theme provides opportunities for children to

- explore and talk about their own feelings about themselves and others.

It provides opportunities for the teacher to

- tackle sensitive issues relating to the possible dangers of child abuse.

- plan positive experiences related to ethnic and racial differences.

Feelings and relationships

14 **What makes me the same as you? What are the feelings we all share? For example, being happy, sad, cheerful, afraid, uneasy, shy, clumsy. What makes us different? How does it feel to be different?**

Activity 1 ● *What makes me the same as you?*

- Talking together. Drawing and painting.

- Individual and small group activities.

Invite the children to draw or paint a portrait of themselves. Display these (without names) asking children to identify themselves and each other if possible. You could contribute a portrait too.

Talk about the portraits and the people they represent. Invite the children to share in making a list of all the ways in which the people in the class are the same. A useful starter might be: 'We are all in the same class'.

Encourage the children to think about the physical attributes they all share, and to widen their thinking and look at activities which are liked by the whole class, for example, PE or story time.

Suggest they think about feelings which they all share at some time or other: love, hate, happiness, sadness, worry, excitement, tiredness or being full of energy.

Children could contribute individual items to a group book entitled 'We are all the same'.

We are all the same   We are happy We are sad We are worried

Activity 2 ● *What feelings do we all share?*

- Talk together, recalling the work on what makes us the same, but focussing on and exploring the feelings we share.

- Small group activity. Talking with individual children.

Invite the children to help make a 'circle of feelings' (making a circle, rather than a list ensures that none are prioritised) start them off by providing one or two, if necessary.

Invite the children to share with each other the times when they have experienced one or more of these feelings by talking, drawing and writing. You could share your own experiences with them too.

There are **cross-curricular links** with:

– movement, drama and role-play.

– literature.

You could create opportunities for one-to-one talks with children who have particular problems and who may need to talk about special feelings.

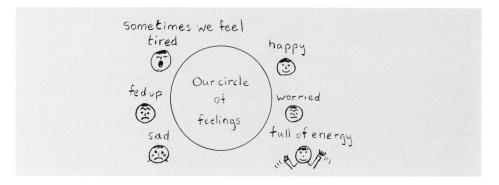

Activity 3 ● *What makes us different?*

- Role-playing. Talking about how different people react to the same situation.
- Class or group activity.

Describe a situation to the children, for example,

– a spider climbing on you.

– being left out or not chosen to play with the others.

– breaking something precious.

– losing something important.

Act out these situations using role-play. Ask the children to talk about how they reacted. Did they all feel the same and do the same thing?

Recall Activity 1. What makes us all the same? Talk about what makes us different, for example, feelings, shape, colour, being the youngest or the oldest.

Emphasise how special it is 'being me', being unique, finding out the special things about 'being me', and valuing these.

It is possible to extend this activity to look at differences in where the children live, how they come to school, the pets they have and their interests. Whichever topic is explored it is important that the children come back to the original theme: that we are in many ways alike, but that each of us is unique and special.

Activity 3 ● *How does it feel to be different?*

- Talking together.
- Group and individual activities.

This aspect of feelings and relationships can be approached in many ways. One way is to approach it through a story or poem about someone, or something being or feeling very different from others, for example the story of The Ugly Duckling.

Invite the children to talk about how such a character might have felt. Was being different a good, or not so good, feeling?

The Ugly Duckling knew he was different

He thought no one liked him

It made him very sad
It wasn't a good feeling

Who made him feel better?

The other swans did

He did

He found he was beautiful

Glen

Feelings and relationships

20 What makes me feel good
about myself and my days?
How do I feel when I feel
good? What can I do to help
make myself feel good?

Activity 1 ● *Feeling good about my days*

● Talking together. Writing and drawing.

● Class or group activity, with the opportunity for individual work.

Invite the children to draw or paint a picture of a good day, one where they felt good about what they had done or what had happened. Invite them to share with others in talk, or through writing, what made it a good day. Help the children write down their ideas, perhaps as the first stage in making a class or group book.

Explore with them the idea of feeling good about oneself and one's day.

Activity 2 ● *Feeling good about myself*

- Use talking together as the starting point for creative activity.
- Individual and shared activity.

Explore further with the children the different kinds of activities which make people feel good, for example, learning a new skill, doing something better than before, helping someone else, making new friends, being more confident and conquering fear.

Invite the children to paint pictures of themselves feeling good. Talk about the feeling and how it is reflected in facial expressions and body language. Talk about how we recognise people feeling good about themselves.

Activity 3 ● *Feeling good about myself*

- Revising and reflecting on what has been learned.
- Shared activity.

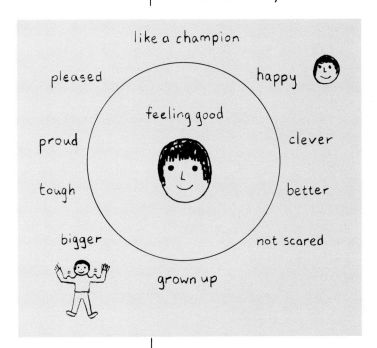

Ask the children to recall some words for feeling good. Collect them into a 'circle of feelings'. Read and reread this, exploring the facial expressions and body language to go with the words.

Ask the children to think of things they can do to help make themselves feel good, for example:

- We can ask someone to join in.
- We can practice and get better at things.
- We can help people and share.
- We can be happy and not worry.
- We can tell people when we are worried.
- We can feel special all day.
- We can keep healthy and happy.

Make a new collection of words and phrases for feeling good.

There are opportunities for extending these activities for children with special needs.

There are **cross-curricular links** with:

- physical education.
- creative activities.
- religious education.
- literature.
- role-play.
- music.
- drama.

Feelings and relationships

36 **Who are our special people and friends? What do they do and say? What do we do together? What do we share or keep secret? What do I like about them, and like doing with them? What makes me scared sometimes or uneasy? Whom can I tell?**

Activity 1 ● *People who are special to me*

- Painting or drawing, leading to talking together.
- Individual and group activities.

Invite the children to draw or paint some of the people who are special to them. Invite them to share by talking or writing what it is that makes each person special. Is it what they do? or say? or feel?

Children will respond with a wide range of suggestions, for example, family and friends, and explanations about being special.

An interesting activity would be to collect their drawings and written explanations and make them into a collage entitled 'These are our special people'. Alternatively, the children could make their own books, in small groups or individually.

Our special people

who are they?   what do we like to do with them?

sit with them in school

share secrets

stay in their houses

play tricks on them

go swimming with them

give them things

visit them

go out with them

have a cuddle

make a gang with them

do dares

swap things

talk to them when we're upset

Talk about the things the children do which make their special people happy, pleased, worried and angry and why this is so. There will be opportunities here to develop some basic ideas on keeping safe, good relationships, and awareness of the impact of one's actions on other people. You could also talk about some rules for keeping safe: saying where you are going, saying 'No' – even if it seems to upset people and about sometimes not keeping secrets.

Talking together, could be valuable at this time, either in small groups, or one-to-one.

There are **cross-curricular links** with:

– literature.

– role-play.

These will provide opportunities for further discussion.

Activity 2 ● *What makes me scared or uneasy?*

- Talking together. Shared writing.
- Small group activity with opportunities for family work.

Recall with the children the previous work on special people and what they enjoy doing for and with them. Remind them that some of their special people can help them when there is a problem, or when they are afraid.

You could use a poem or story in which fear is overcome or where a child character admits to fear and tells a special person.

Talk with the children about real fears and hazards in comparison with pretend or imaginary ones, for example, 'monsters'. You could share some of your own fears, both real and imaginary, with them.

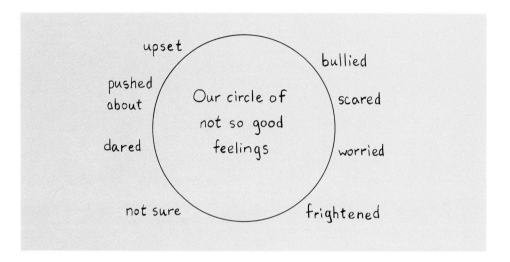

Write and draw a 'circle of not-so-good feelings', inviting the children to illustrate how the words and phrases are communicated by facial expressions, gestures, and body language. Talk with them about *when* they feel this way and write up their responses on a chart or blackboard.

You will know whether it is likely that the children will respond with statements similar to those in the illustration above or whether it would be appropriate to ask 'What if . . .'

Role-play one or more of the situations suggested by these activities. Invite the children to try out ways in which the problem could be resolved. What could they say or do? Whom could they ask for help? How would they ask for help or tell someone?

Invite them to work in pairs practising these strategies. Offer some phrases they could start with, for example, 'Please listen', or 'I want to tell you something', or 'I'm worried and scared about something, will you listen?'

Family work: take the opportunities which arise when planning and exploring these themes to negotiate with, and enlist support from, the children's families and the community.

8 & 9

Action planner
Me & looking after myself

1

My healthy lifestyle: what do I do, or think I do, to make and keep myself healthy? What don't I do? Why? How do I know? Is there anything I can change?

2

What do I think adults, the young and the old do to make and keep themselves healthy? What don't they do? What are their messages to us? Do different people have different messages? What are they?

3

My healthy body – inside and out. What are its everyday needs? What are its occasional needs? (For example, dental check-ups.) What can be my responsibility?

4

To keep my body healthy I need to know:
- about healthy eating;
- about what my body does with the food I eat;
- about the other things I take into my body (accidentally or on purpose) and how my body reacts to them;
- about germs, how they get into my body, what they do and about my very

important 'germ busters' (immune system);
- about exercise and what happens to my body when I exercise.
- about my healthy heart;
- about fresh air, smoke and the other things I might breathe in;
- about caring for my body.

5

What do we mean by 'not so healthy'? Can people who are old or disabled be healthy?

6

What do I do to keep myself safe? What do I think I have to keep safe from?

7

What body changes do I see in the people around me as they grow, age and become pregnant? What changes are going on inside me?

8

How do babies begin? How are they born? How do they grow and develop? Who cares for them? How are they cared for?

9

Whose job is it to keep me healthy? How can I take on some responsibility for my own healthy lifestyle?

10

How can I help protect my body and look after it? How can I help with hygiene, simple first aid, rest and relaxation? What happens when I take pills and medicines which are prescribed for me?

11

What about my brain? How can I help my brain to work well?

What are the words I need to know:

– to talk about my body and how it works?

– to describe the hazards to my body?

– to talk about being and keeping safe?

– to talk about changing and growing?

Classroom strategies and activities for ages 8 and 9

● *Key themes*

The following pages describe in detail activities related to three key themes for this age group:

Themes	Content boxes
Taking responsibility for my healthy lifestyle	(25)→(9)→(15) (see page 89)
Feeling (including loss, separation and relationships)	(13)→(19) (see page 97)
My healthy body (including healthy eating, exercise, my healthy heart and dealing with germs)	(4) (see page 103)

It is important that you select and modify these activities according to your needs. If you are devising your own health education programme you may be well aware of the health education priorities of your school, and may have selected the key themes you wish to explore with your pupils. If this is the case, you may find that the following activities are useful examples. On the other hand, you may wish to incorporate them as they stand in your programme.

All the themes are explored through the content boxes which act as starting points for the activities. There are three other key themes relevant to this age group for which you may wish to plan your own activities:

Photocopy

Me & my relationships

12   What makes and keeps me happy, safe and feeling good? Is feeling good the same as feeling happy?

13   What makes me feel sad? unsure? lonely? embarrassed? What makes other people feel like that? What can I do to feel better? What can I do for other people?

14   What can I do (or learn to do) when I'm frightened? lost? bullied? upset? teased? dared? What makes me feel confident with people in difficult situations, for example, coping with dares and boasting. Who can help me?

15   Who and what are the 'persuaders'? Can I be persuaded by other people, or by television, to change my healthy lifestyle? How do I know what to believe? How do I know what they are *really* saying? What is real? factual? imaginary? a matter of opinion?

16   How do I feel about being me? How do I feel about being this sex? size? shape? colour? What do I think about my feelings, my fears, my friends?

17   How do I feel about other people? How do I feel about people who are like me and people who are different from me? What makes them different? How can I get to know them better?

18   What can I do to feel good? How can I spread this feeling? What do others do to make me feel good? What do I do to make them feel good? How do I know I'm feeling good and on top of the world?

19   How do I feel when I lose special things, break up with friends, or I am separated from people I love because they go away or die? Who can help me? How can I learn to cope?

20   What is a 'grown-up'? What do grown-ups *have* to do or be responsible for? How do I know that I am growing up? What are the special landmarks in my life? How do I feel about growing up and changing? What helps me to grow up, for example, sharing, finding out, knowing what's happening?

21   What risks can I take? Who will stand by me? How can I be safe?

22   Who are my special people and special friends? How do I feel about belonging? Do I have different feelings for my friends, for my family and for other people? Do they have different feelings for me? What is a friend? Do friends 'owe' me anything? What do I 'owe' them?

What are the words I need to know:

– to talk about my own, and others' feelings, such as love, anger and loss?

– to talk about changing feelings?

– to talk about differences between people?

8 & 9

Me & my community & environment

23 Who are the people who work to keep me and other people healthy and safe?

24 Where do these people work? Can we go to these places, talk to these people, and find out what they do?

25 Is ours a health-promoting class? Is ours a health-promoting school? What can I do to help? What are my responsibilities in, and out of, school?

26 Real and imaginary people, places, lifestyles and situations. I need to be honest and realistic about real and imaginary things. Who are my special people? What are my special places and belongings? I want people to respect my things and my privacy. Secret places, feelings and activities. When should I keep secrets? When should I tell about secret people and secret places?

27 It is important to know how and when to say: 'Yes', 'No', 'No, you can't', 'No, I won't', 'That won't work', 'Don't', 'Please stop', 'I don't do dares'.

28 There are many kinds of people in the community, living many different lifestyles. We need to value all people, what they are and what they do.

29 How do I know where and how to find people to keep me safe and healthy? How do I recognise them? How do I ask them for help?

30 Who are the people who need special care? What can I learn about them? What can I do to help?

31 Where do I get the food I need to eat? For example, shops, cafés, food stalls. What kind of food do they sell? Is it fresh? Who chooses the food I eat? Can I choose for myself? What helps me to choose? What do I need to know? Who will guide me?

32 Who are the people who keep my home, school and play areas healthy, safe and free from vandals? How do I help (or hinder) these people? How can I protect myself, other people and the environment? How can I spread the message?

33 What do I think are dangerous places, objects and situations? How do I recognise them? We need to keep dangerous things in safe places, for example, tablets should be kept in a medicine cabinet. How do I think I keep safe? What more can I do?

34 What do I think are risky or dangerous situations? How can I ask for help? Who are the best people to ask for help? When is it safe to take responsibility for myself and others? When is it risky?

What are the words I need to know to describe:

– the people in the community, their language and lifestyles?

– places and situations?

– feelings, fears and reactions?

Themes	Content boxes
Growing, changing and growing up	20 → 7 → 8 → 26
Health hazards (including smoking, and the role of medicines and drugs)	10 → 33 → 15 → 34
Keeping safe*	6 → 23 → 33 → 27 → 21

(A summary of the main strategies and activities used in this chapter can be found on page 172).

(*Additional material provided in Health for Life 2.)

Theme *Taking responsibility for my healthy lifestyle*

Use content boxes 25, 9 and 15:

25

Is ours a health-promoting class? Is ours a health-promoting school? What can I do to help? What are my responsibilities in, and out of, school?

→

9

Whose job is it to keep me healthy? How can I take on some responsibility for my own healthy lifestyle?

→

15

Who and what are the 'persuaders'? Can I be persuaded by other people, or by television, to change my healthy lifestyle? How do I know what to believe? How do I know what they are *really* saying? What is real? factual? imaginary? a matter of opinion?

This theme provides opportunities to explore:

- the interdependence of people.
- the extent to which the children themselves can be responsible for their healthy lifestyle and environment.
- peer and media pressure.

Taking responsibility for my healthy lifestyle

25 **Is ours a health-promoting class? Is ours a health-promoting school? What can I do to help? What are my responsibilities in, and out of, school?**

Activity 1 ● *Is ours a health-promoting school?*

- Talking together, leading to organising and grouping children's responses according to given criteria.

- Group activity with opportunities for individual work.

Talk with the children, or hold a brainstorming session, and discuss questions such as:

'What would a healthy school

– look like?'

– do?'

– not do?'

– have?'

and, 'What would you see happening, or not happening?'

A healthy school:

Safe clean lots of space accident proof friendly people fresh air in it light happy everyone counts not too noisy no bullies hardworking no vandalism people help you kind teachers everyone knows the health rules teaches health

Write down the children's responses to these questions in random order. Introduce the idea that it is good for everyone in the school to know the school's 'health rules'.

Invite the children to sort and group their responses, for example, which responses are concerned with the way people behave to each other? Which responses are concerned with the building?

Suggest they go back to the idea of 'health rules' and make a checklist of these for themselves and for the school.

Activity 2 ●   *What can I do to help?*

- Individual or group work. Talking together.

- Group activity with opportunities for role-play, family involvement and presentation work.

Suggest to the children that they use their checklist to look at their own school or classroom. (It is useful to warn other people on the staff about this!)

Come together to share what they have discovered. What do they think needs to be changed? What do they think can be changed? What can they do now? Where can they start? How can they let others know what they are doing?

This would be an opportunity to work in groups, making group plans like the one below.

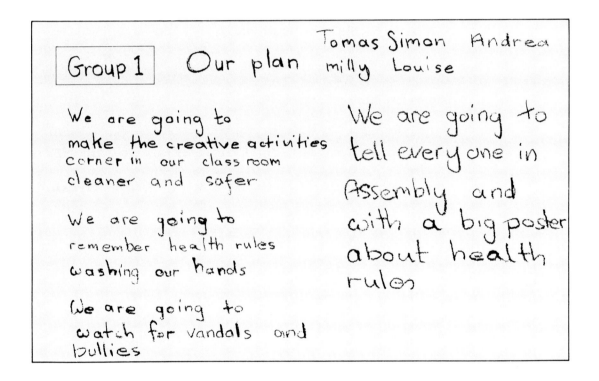

You could set a date to review the plans, using the original checklist again and look for positive signs of improvement.

There are opportunities for children to role-play decision-making activities in which they explore the roles of people in the school and community who make decisions about the health of the school.

There are opportunities too for family work. Children could take home their plans and explain them to their families and ask them for support. This activity could provide the springboard for presenting this theme to the whole school, with your class as the 'experts' able to pass on the important messages.

Taking responsibility for my healthy lifestyle

9 **Whose job is it to keep me healthy? How can I take on some responsibility for my own healthy lifestyle?**

Activity 1 ● *Whose job is it to keep me healthy? How can I take on some responsibility?*

- Investigating the children's perceptions of the people whose job it is to keep them healthy using the Draw and Write Investigation Technique (see Appendix 1, page 176). Analysing and displaying the children's drawing and writing, leading to class or group discussion.

- Class, group and individual activities.

Invite the children to take part in a survey and tell them that the work should be done individually and without conferring. Ask them to draw and label the people whose job it is to keep children healthy.

Ask the children to share in analysing the results of the survey. The results can be categorised and displayed on a chart like the one below (your class might want to include other categories such as water board engineers or refuse collectors). The ticks below each category represent the number of children who included it in their work.

Parents or grown ups	Teachers	Doctors	Nurses	Dentists	Scientists	SELF
✓ ✓ ✓ ✓ ✓ ✓ ✓ ✓ ✓	✓ ✓ ✓	✓ ✓ ✓ ✓ ✓ ✓ ✓ ✓ ✓ ✓ ✓ ✓	✓ ✓ ✓	✓ ✓ ✓ ✓ ✓ ✓ ✓ ✓	✓ ✓	✓ ✓ ✓ ✓ ✓ ✓ ✓ ✓ ✓ ✓ ✓ ✓

Invite the children to talk about the results, particularly the category which they think is the most important.

Invite the children to talk about the results, particularly the category which they think is the most important.
healthy lifestyles. This provides an opportunity to involve visitors and visits.

Talk with the children about their responsibility to make these people's jobs easier. Introduce the idea that this includes learning more about the way their own bodies work.

You can extend this work to include the environment. Ask the children to think about the people who keep the environment healthy. What can they do to help? Explore with them the practical things they can do, such as:

— picking up litter;

— caring for plants, trees and buildings;

— not destroying or defacing property.

Look at matters of attitude, such as:

— valuing and enjoying the environment;

— setting good examples, especially to younger children;

— supporting those who work for environmental health.

There are **cross-curricular links** with:

— environmental studies. (This could include visits, visitors, local studies, work on pollution and conservation, and individual and group topic work.)

— family involvement.

— creative activities, including classroom play and role-play.

Taking responsibility for my healthy lifestyle

15 **Who and what are the 'persuaders'? Can I be persuaded by other people, or by television, to change my healthy lifestyle? How do I know what to believe? How do I know what they are *really* saying? What is real? factual? imaginary? a matter of opinion?**

Activity 1 ● *Let's persuade!*

- Devising an advertising campaign to sell a new item. Discussing the techniques which are used to persuade people to buy things.

- Class and group activities with an opportunity for family work.

Invite the class or group to help you devise an advertising campaign for a new chocolate bar called 'Chocalump'. Ask the children to suggest ways in which they could persuade people to buy 'Chocalump'. Explore questions such as:

– Which methods work best on children?

– Which methods work best on grown-ups?

– Why do they work?

– Do we believe everything they say?

– Why not?

– Who might?

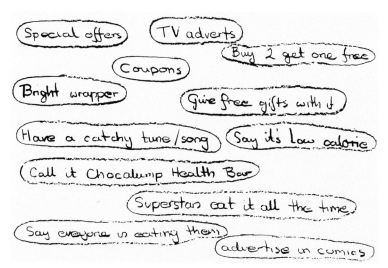

Invite the children to devise a poster or a television advertisement which will persuade people to buy 'Chocalump'. The children could take home their work and explain it to their families to see if they would be persuaded to buy the chocolate bar.

Activity 2 ● *Being persuaded*

- Role-play and discussion on persuasion in a health and safety context and how to counter such persuasion.

- Pair and group activities with the opportunity for individual and family work.

Invite the children to imagine situations in which someone is trying to persuade them to do something which could be dangerous, stupid, unhealthy and irresponsible. Ask them to make a list of these situations.

Invite the children to work in pairs. Ask each pair to choose one of these situations for a role-play in which one child is the 'persuader' and the other child is the 'persuaded'. Suggest they start by thinking about what people say when they are persuading others to do something they don't want to do. After the role-plays, ask the children to come together as a class, or in groups, to make a list of persuasive statements.

— What people say to persuade you —

if you don't do it you're not my friend

Yellow Coward

You did it last time so why not now

Go on everyone else does it

Go on. you've seen them do it on TV

Just this once you'll be OK

No one else will see – this is just the right place

you'll be the only one

You can't be in the gang

I promise I won't tell

Encourage the children to read through the statements using their most persuasive manner. Talk with them about how it feels when these things are said to them.

Explore ways of answering persuasive people which are assertive and unapologetic. Talk about starting a refusal with the word 'No' or 'No thanks', rather than working up to it and putting it at the end of a sentence. Acknowledge that refusing to be persuaded can be difficult. Make a note of responses like the ones below and practise them with the children. Recall previous work on the theme: 'Who keeps me healthy?' Recall ideas of personal responsibility. Discuss who has the ultimate responsibility for being, or not being, persuaded. This could be followed up with language work. Ask the children to plan and write dialogues for other children to role-play. They could describe the situation and the characters and set out the dialogue.

What can you say to a persuader?

No I don't believe that

No. I think it's a stupid idea I'm not the only one

No thanks, I don't know enough about it

If that's the kind of gang, I don't think I want to be in it

You can't be much of a friend if you ask me that

I won't like being left out, but its better than doing something stupid

That's not true.

What's being a coward got to do with being sensible?

The children's families might be interested to see this work. You could ask them to suggest other situations which the children might have to face and which could be explored in the same way.

At this stage children can benefit from talking about what they see happening on television, at school and at home, not only in terms of recognising 'persuaders', but in terms of distinguishing between the real and the fictional or 'pretend'. Discuss questions such as 'Were these people expressing their own feelings or were they acting parts written for them?' Children need to be encouraged to talk about their own feelings, especially those related to peer pressure, and to find the most appropriate and useful words to convey what they feel.

They need to know that in order to be responsible and not to be pushed or pressured, they may have to pretend to have strong brave feelings and that most people, adults too, have to do this, and practise until they become good at it.

Encourage them to talk with each other about these feelings and to identify adults in the home, at school, and in the community, who could listen to them and help them.

Use content boxes 13 and 19:

13

What makes me feel sad? unsure? lonely? embarrassed? What makes other people feel like that? What can I do to feel better? What can I do for other people?

19

How do I feel when I lose special things, break up with friends, or I am separated from people I love because they go away or die? Who can help me? How can I learn to cope?

This is a sensitive area of personal and family life, but it is one which children do indicate quite strongly that they wish to talk about and share with others. The suggested activities are for small groups of children and are designed to provide opportunities for this sharing.

You will know if, and when, and with which children, this kind of activity would be appropriate and where it would be more important to provide a time for individuals to talk privately to you.

You can provide the children with early opportunities to share their feelings about loss and separation when they are 4 or 5 years old. This work can be reinforced when they are 6 or 7 years old (see the Action Planners for these age ranges). This early work will provide a firm basis for the activities at this stage.

Feelings (including loss, separation and relationships)

 What makes me feel sad? unsure? lonely? embarassed? What makes other people feel like that? What can I do to feel better? What can I do for other people?

Activity 1 ● *What makes me feel sad? unsure? lonely? embarrassed?*

- Class work. Using children's literature as the starting point for a discussion about different feelings, go on to make a 'circle of feelings' chart.

- Individual and group work with opportunities for drawing, writing role-playing and talking together.

Read a story, poem or song to the children in which the character feels some of these emotions, for example, The Ugly Duckling and Rudolf the Red Nosed Reindeer. Ask the children to make a note of the different feelings mentioned in the story while they are listening. Collect the children's notes and use them as the basis of a 'circle of feelings' like the one below:

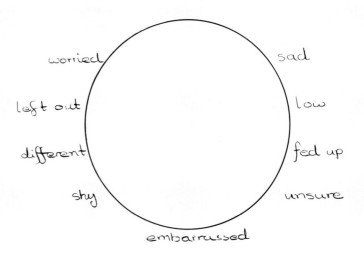

Invite the children to explain when and why the character felt like this using talking, drawing and writing, or role-playing.

You can extend this activity by discussing with the children questions such as:

- Did the character feel like this because of what someone was saying or doing?

- Did the character imagine the problem or lack confidence?

- Would it have helped if the character had known someone else with the same problem? How would it have helped?

Continue the talk by inviting the children to recall times when they had experienced these feelings. Which words in the 'circle of feelings' would they use to describe how they felt?

Encourage the children to consider:

— Who or what helped the character to feel better?

— Who or what helped *them* to feel better?

— Does it help to know that someone else has been through the same problem?

Activity 2 ● *When do other people feel sad? unsure? lonely? embarrassed?*

● Group or individual work. Collecting or cutting-out pictures, or drawing and painting.

● Group work. Talking together, making up stories and using and extending the 'circle of feelings' from Activity 1.

Ask the children to collect pictures of people who are embarrassed, unhappy, lonely, alone, unsure and 'mixed up'. Alternatively, you can ask them to draw and paint pictures of these people. Invite them to talk about the pictures and speculate, or make up stories about the situations which caused the people in the pictures to feel this way. Use the vocabulary in the 'circle of feelings' from Activity 1 and extend it if necessary.

Ask the children to work in pairs or small groups and write a story around the situation in the picture. Ask them to finish the stories with, firstly, a good ending, and secondly, an ending which is not so good. Ask them questions such as 'If you had been there, what would you have said or done?'

Our picture was a man going away from two children they all look sad

This is our good ending

the children went to their grans for tea and talked to her and felt better

I would have said come and play at my house you can tell my mum if you like

This is our not so good ending they thought they were the only ones it happened to and got more and more sad

I would have said lets go and play football you'll feel better in the morning

Ruth and Julie

Feelings (including loss, separation and relationships)

 How do I feel when I lose special things, break up with friends, or I am separated from people I love because they go away or die? Who can help me? How can I learn to cope?

Activity 1 ● *What do loss and separation feel like?*

● Again, children's literature can provide a starting point. It is not necessary to use stories which have been written specifically about loss and separation, though these have their place. You can use stories where the characters experience these feelings or situations as part of a wider theme.

You will find that your children's librarian can provide you with a range of such books, stories and poems, and/or a bibliography.

● Group activity. Making, and talking about, a 'circle of feelings' which describes a character in the story. There are opportunities for mime or role-play.

Read your chosen story, part of a story, or poem, to the children. Invite them to put themselves into the role of the character who suffered loss of some kind, and talk about what the character felt.

With the children make a 'circle of feelings' for that character and invite them to interpret these feelings using drawing, or mime and body language.

Encourage them to extend their vocabulary: ask them to look at the 'circle of feelings' and to replace basic words such as 'sad' or 'unhappy' with a variety of words and expressions. Invite them to imagine the possible reasons behind specific feelings.

Activity 2 ● *How do I feel when I lose things?*

- Talking together, exploring and extending the language of the emotions. Sharing perceptions of loss.

- Class or small group activity leading to individual activity.

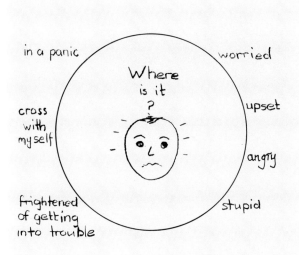

Invite the children to think of an everyday object that they might lose, or have lost in the past, for example, a purse, a key, a coat, a lunch box, a toy, a book. Ask how they might feel, or felt. With the children compare the feelings associated with this kind of loss with those associated with losing or being separated from people. How are they different?

Explore with the children the idea of relief: ask them to think of words to describe how they feel when they find that missing object.

Invite them to illustrate and write about losing and finding something, or losing something and *not* finding it, and about how they felt. Ask the children if they are willing to share what they have written with other children.

Activity 3 ● *How do I feel when I lose, or am separated from, people?*

- Talking together and sharing feelings, with the opportunity to do some shared or individual writing.

- Class, group and individual activity.

Invite the children to repeat Activity 2, but this time to explore the feelings they had about:

- the loss of a pet, and finding, or not finding, it again.

- the loss of a friend who has moved away or changed schools.

- the loss of someone special who has gone away for a short time.

- 'falling out' with a friend and losing a friendship.

Encourage the children to widen their vocabulary of words associated with feelings, and to share and explore the difference between the emotions of temporary and permanent loss.

Activity 4 ● *Who can help me?*

- Sharing ideas of how people can help in times of distress, loss or separation.

- Small group activity. A time for very personal sharing through talking, drawing and writing.

Ask the children to describe individually, in drawing and writing, who had helped them, and how they had felt, when they lost something or someone in the past.

When I lost my dog my family helped me look for him.

The policeman said he would report it

My friend Kim kept cheering me up

I was useless, I cried and cried and so did our baby →

He came back ! I cried again.

Invite the children to help to make two lists:

− People who can help me.

− How I can help myself.

People who can help
My family
My friends
Other grown ups
My teacher
myself

How I can help myself ?
I can tell some one about it
I can have a good cry
I can paint a picture
I can keep busy
I can write about it
I can read about how it happens to someone else

Painting, drama and play can provide children with additional opportunities to explore their own and others' feelings in this sensitive area.

Theme ● *My healthy body (food, drugs, exercise)*

Use content box 4:

To keep my body healthy I need to know:

- about healthy eating;
- about what my body does with the food I eat;
- about the other things I take into my body (accidentally or on purpose) and how my body reacts to them;
- about germs, how they get into my body, what they do and about my very important 'germ busters' (immune system);
- about exercise, and what happens to my body when I exercise;
- about my healthy heart;
- about fresh air, smoke and the other things I might breathe in;
- about caring for my body.

Box 4 can be linked with content boxes 1, 3, 7, 9, 10, 11 and 29.

This is a very wide content area. It offers you opportunities to:

- take a very broad look at the body in the context of the three basic content areas: *Me and looking after myself, Me and my relationships* and *Me and my community and environment* (see page 15).

- focus on particular areas of concern, for example, *substance abuse, smoking,* the importance of maintaining the body's *immune system,* the approach to *puberty,* a healthy *heart.*

There are **cross-curricular links** with science, particularly biology, in all these activities.

Activity 1 ● ***What do I need to know to keep healthy?***

- Exploring and increasing children's awareness of what they think they need to know in order to have a healthy body and a healthy lifestyle. Making a list of the topics they need to find out more about.

- Class, group and individual activities.

Initiate a brainstorming session based on the question 'What do you think *you* need to know about your body if you are going to make and keep it healthy?' This is an opportunity for children to work in small groups and then report back to you and the rest of the class.

Invite the children to make a list of their responses to this question and check that they have covered all aspects of the issue. Ask them to put the topics on the list in order of importance and to suggest some possible sources of information.

Activity 2 ● ***Healthy eating***

- Investigate how children explain why we need to eat and drink.

- Class, group and individual activities.

Invite the children to take part in a survey entitled 'Why do we need to eat and drink?' Ask them to write about, and illustrate, the reasons. Explain the 'rules' of the survey to them: they must not discuss the question with each other, they must work alone, and they need not name their papers.

Analyse the children's responses with their help. Encourage them to use some of the following categories to code the papers:

- Growth

- Body repair

- Nutrition

- Energy

- Staying alive

- Body health

- Feeling good

- Looking good

- Enjoyment

This activity could be repeated using the question 'What is *in* food and drink which makes and keeps us healthy?'

By this stage children will have internalised many messages about healthy eating, some of these may be contradictory and some may have been misinterpreted. To avoid further confusion, it is important to start with the children's own explanations and language and use this as a base for new information. This survey will reveal the children's perceptions and explanations.

Activity 3 ● *How can we eat for health?*

- Finding out which foods children think are healthy, and not so healthy.
- Individual activity followed by sharing and talking together.

On one half of a piece of paper, ask the children to draw and label foods which they think they should eat more often, and on the other half, ask them to draw and label foods with which they think they should be more cautious.

Invite the children to share in presenting and analysing their responses. Encourage them to use these categories to code the papers:

- Fruit

- Bread and cereals

- Pulses and grains

- Other foods

- Fibre

- Fatty foods

- Sugary foods and drinks

- Salt

You could make a list of useful words and write them in a wordbox on the blackboard.

Word box		
diet	glucose	too much
pasta	whole foods	too little
syrup	not enough	

Ask the children to go through their work again and look for everyday examples from their own diets. Invite them to talk about when and where they eat and drink these foods.

Encourage them to talk together about their diets. Listen for the most common, and uncommon, statements they make about their diets.

Talk with the children about the sources of their views on healthy and not so healthy foods. 'Who says so?' can be a useful question.

Activity 4 ● *How can I eat for health?*

● Discussing eating habits and how to change them. Devising personal 'contracts'.

● Shared activity followed by individual and family work.

Invite the children to review the list made in Activity 3 and use it to look at their own eating patterns. Do they think they need to make any changes in their eating lifestyles? What changes can they realistically make?

Suggest that each child makes a personal (folded paper) book in which they can record the changes they plan to make. They can also use it to 'tick-off' the changes they achieve.

In addition, you could suggest that each child makes a personal Eating for Health Contract in which they promise themselves that they will try to change their eating habits. Talk together as a class about who might help the children to keep the contract, both at school and at home.

Family work: children might like to take home the book and contract to show to their families. You could suggest that the children explain to their families what they are doing and enlist their help.

Activity 5 ● *What happens to the food inside me?*

- Using drawing and writing activities to discover the children's perceptions of digestion.
- Individual activity leading to discussion.

Children's perceptions of the digestive system will vary widely. Rather than offer children a model or diagram of the system as a starting point, it can be more useful to discover what they think happens by asking them to write about, and illustrate, what happens during digestion. Once you have the results of the investigation, you will be able to match your chosen factual information to the children's own conceptual level.

Invite the children to draw themselves eating some food they enjoy, and then ask them to draw the food as it goes through their digestive system.

Invite them to show in their drawings, if they can, how food fulfils all the functions listed in Activity 2, for example, repair, enjoyment, energy, looking good etc. Invite the children to share their work with each other. Ask them to look for and explain the most common, and the most unusual, features of their drawings.

This is the stage when it is relevant to introduce a model of the digestive system to the children. At this point they should be able to follow a more scientific explanation and you can introduce biological vocabulary. The amount of time spent on this will vary for each class or group.

Activity 6 ● *What happens to the food inside me? (Becoming an 'expert')*

● Extending the children's vocabulary of the digestive system. Exploring ways of illustrating and presenting information.

● Individual, group and family work.

As they learn, children will enjoy discovering how 'expert' they have become in handling the language associated with healthy eating and the digestive system. Ask them to compare their 'pre-expert' and 'post-expert' vocabulary.

With the children, look at the journey made by food as it is broken down and used by the body. Invite them to think of ways of presenting this information, both as a reminder for themselves, and as an explanation for others, for example, it could be presented as:

— a shared wall story composed of pictures and writing which can be shared with other classes in the school.

— individual folded paper books which children can take home to share with their families.

This activity could be tackled in small groups, with each group choosing its own method of presentation and sharing the completed work with the rest of the class.

Activity 7 ● *How do substances apart from food enter my body?*

● Exploring children's perceptions and increasing their awareness of dangerous substances.

● Class or group activity with opportunities for individual work. Family work is essential if substance abuse is to be tackled at this point.

Invite the children to talk about what they take into their bodies apart from food. Discuss questions such as:

— How do I do this?

— Do I always have the choice? What substances enter my body accidentally? What substances do I purposely put into my body?

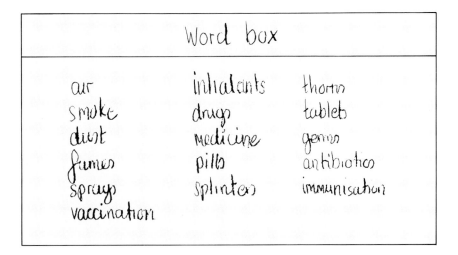

This is a good time to introduce the topic of drugs. Talk to the children about the difference between what are popularly known as 'drugs', and medicines. What do pharmaceutical companies, chemists, doctors and nurses mean by drugs? What do television and other media sources often mean when they use the word?

Ask the children to recall times when they had to take medicine in any form. Ask questions, such as: Why did you have to take it? How often did you take it? Where did the medicine come from? Who went to get it? Who said you should take it? Who gave it to you? Why did you stop taking the medicine? What did it do for you? How do you think it worked inside your body?

Once again it is important for the children to have the opportunity to share their perceptions of what medicines are, and what they do, and to discover that other children may have different views.

Invite the children to work in pairs or small groups and make a list of Drug Rules.

Family work: suggest that the children take home their Drug Rules, explain them to their families and ask them for their comments.

For more activities on drugs, see the accompanying book, *Health for Life 2 – Health education in the primary school: a teacher's guide to three key topics.*

There is a **cross-curricular link** here with the study of pollution. You could explore how pollution affects the body and how it can be prevented.

Activity 8 ● *Body systems*

- Using the children's individual drawing and writing to discover their perceptions.

- Talking together.

At this stage children could explore other systems of the body such as, circulation or respiration, using questions like these as a starting point.
What goes into my body and how does it get in?
What does it do there?

It is important to tap the children's perceptions and explanations of their body systems, and again, the children's own diagrams, and written explanations will be very revealing. (The sections of the *My Body Project* which tackle body systems could be used at this stage. See Appendix 2, page 188.)

This would, for some groups, be an appropriate time to look in greater depth at two aspects of medicines and drugs:

- how medicines, pills and injections enter the bloodstream and make them feel better.

- how dangerous substances enter the bloodstream and the effect they may have on one's thinking, behaviour and health.

- Discussing and making the children more aware of, the body's defence systems. Making shared or individual pictorial diagrams and explanations.

- Class or group activity, with opportunities for individual and family work.

Useful starters to this activity could come from history and geography, using studies of strategically-built castles, invasions etc, and biology and zoology, using studies of animal and insect defence systems, such as bee stings and camouflage.

Recall with the children their previous work on how different substances enter the body. Reinforce previous discussion about 'accidentally' and 'on purpose'. Invite the children to share their views about the body's outer defences. What stops dust, dirt, water and other substances from getting into the body?

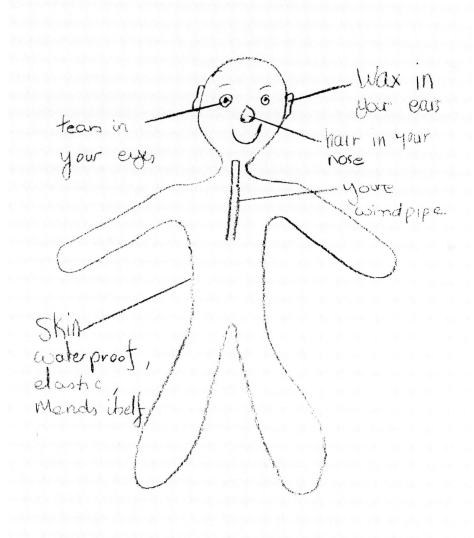

Ask the children to draw diagrams of the body, working either individually or in pairs. Ask them to use annotations to highlight the body's natural defences such as skin, tears, earwax etc.

Ask them to come together and share their work. Encourage them to add to their diagrams during the discussion or to contribute to a large-size class version which you can draw.

How can I help my outside defence system?

I can understand how my body works

germs
dirt
drugs

I keep healthy so my skin mends quickly

I don't push things up my nose in my ears

I keep my body clean

I don't stick things into my skin

I don't sniff dangerous things or things I don't know

I don't poke people in the eye

I don't let people make me do things like sniff or smoke

I tell someone if I cut myself or anything like that

Invite the children to suggest ways in which they can assist their bodies' defence systems and to write these down.

Family work: children could take home their individual versions of the diagram, explain them to their families, and invite them to make contributions.

Activity 10 ● *My inner defence system*

- Discussing the body's inner defence system. Shared or individual drawing and written work.

- Class or group activity with opportunities for individual and family work.

Build on the children's work on the outer defence systems when introducing the inner defence systems. Invite the children to write about and illustrate their ideas of what these systems do.

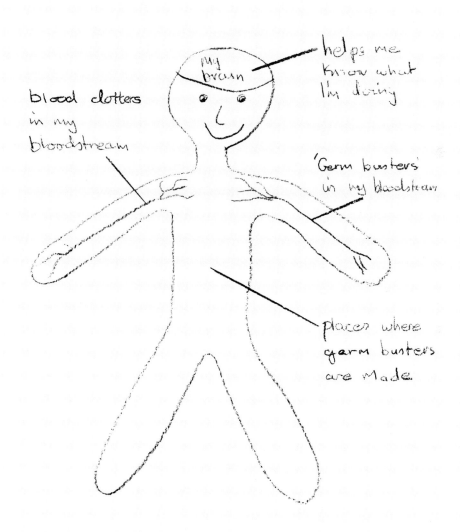

Children could build up folders of work relating to the defence systems of their bodies and take these home to share with their families.

When discussing or explaining the body's defence systems, it is important to emphasise the role played by the immune system (or 'germ busters') and the importance of maintaining the body's ability to produce them. This would provide a foundation for later teaching about AIDS, or could be used to help you answer some of the children's questions about this issue.

This approach can be explained to parents, governors and health professionals to demonstrate how the issues of substance abuse and AIDS can be introduced to children.

Invite the children to explore the question: What can I do to help my inner defence system? These are some of the answers you can discuss with them:

— Have a healthy lifestyle, a healthy diet and exercise.

— Learn as much as I can about the way my body works.

— Keep myself, my possessions and environment as healthy as possible.

— Avoid the introduction of dangerous substances into my body.

— Ask questions when I see, or hear, things I don't understand.

— Try to understand about vaccination and immunisation.

— Try not to pass on germs.

— Wash my hands after using the lavatory and playing with pets, and before eating or handling food.

— Keep food clean and covered.

— Do as instructed when I am ill.

There are **cross-curricular links** with:

— science, exploring the story of pioneers like Louis Pasteur.

— geography, looking at Third World countries in which some people suffer from famine, poverty, and diseases which have been eradicated in developed countries.

Activity 11 ● *What exercise do I take?*

● Organising group and class surveys. Discussing, analysing and presenting the results.

● Class and group activities with an opportunity for family work.

Invite the children to write about and illustrate all the different kinds of exercise they enjoy.

Ask them to get into small groups and collate and present their work so that they can share it with other groups. Ask the children to suggest categories for classifying the illustrated exercises, for example, cycling, swimming, running, aerobics, dancing and team sports, with perhaps a 'general' category for less popular exercises.

Bring together the results of the group surveys and make a class chart which shows the popularity of each type of exercise. Talk with the children about the results.

Exercise we enjoy

swimming	cycling	running	team games	aerobics dancing	general
✓✓✓✓✓	✓✓✓	✓✓✓✓✓	✓✓✓		✓✓✓✓
✓✓✓✓✓	✓✓✓	✓✓✓✓✓	✓✓✓	✓ ✓	✓✓✓
✓✓	✓✓	✓✓✓✓	✓✓✓	✓✓	✓✓✓✓
		✓			
12	**8**	**15**	**9**	**4**	**11**

– riding
– skating
– gymnastics
– weight lifting
– judo

We decided that we could only put 3 exercises each to make it fair.

Can you see which was the most popular? the least popular?

6 people said they didn't enjoy exercise at all!

What would be your message to them? | Hey ------------ ! |

The children could widen the scope of the survey by asking other people in the school, parents and/or older siblings what types of exercise they enjoy.

Using pictorial representation methods to present the survey results provides a **cross-curricular link** with mathematics.

Activity 12 ● Exercise makes me feel . . .

- Using language activities to encourage children to extend the vocabulary they use to describe their feelings.

- Class or group activities with an opportunity for individual work.

You could take as your starting point any recent period of exercise, PE lesson or outdoor activity in which the children were involved.

Invite the children to recall the feelings they experienced both during and after the exercise.

Using the children's own words, write a 'circle of feelings'. Encourage them to use new words and phrases and add them to the circle.

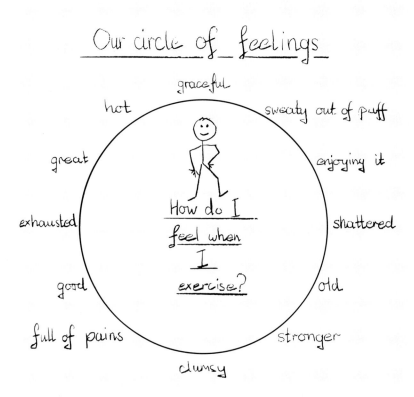

Suggest that the children write and illustrate a series of sentences to describe how they felt during exercise using some of this vocabulary.

There are **cross-curricular links** with:

– painting and collage making, using exercise as a theme.

– PE

Activity 13 ● *What happens when I exercise?*

● Investigation followed by recording and presentation. Group discussion leading to the choosing of presentation methods as 'experts'.

● Class or group work, with an opportunity for family work.

Again use some recent physical activity as your starting point, and remind the children of the 'circle of feelings' made in Activity 12.

Which of these words and phrases describe how their *bodies* feel during exercise? For example, hot, sweaty, clumsy, out of breath. Which of the words and phrases describe how they feel *mentally*? For example, happy, good, graceful.

Return to the children's descriptions of how their bodies feel and use these as a starting point for exploring the physical processes connected with exercise. Ask them to think about what happens to their limbs, muscles, heart and lungs during exercise. For example, the heart beats faster, the muscles stretch and get tired, breathing is quicker.

Help the children to investigate how and why these processes happen, and use the new information they gather to write and illustrate individual summaries entitled 'What happens when I exercise?'

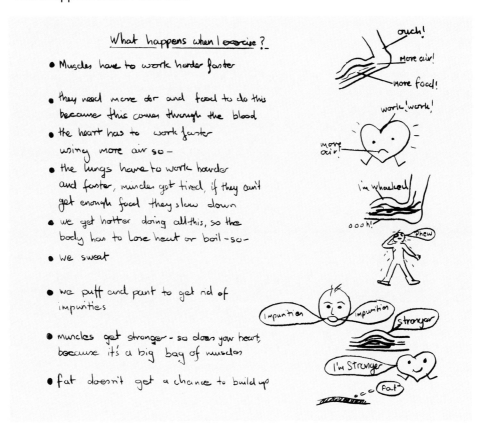

Invite the children to think of ways of presenting and explaining to others what they have learned. For example, the information could be presented

— as a wall story;

— at an assembly;

— as a class, group or individual book, to be passed round, and taken home;

— as a series of short talks given by individuals or groups;

— to parents or friends;

— in mime.

There are **cross-curricular links** with:

— science and mathematics (measuring speed, distance and endurance, taking one's pulse, timing, estimating and checking.)

— creative activities.

Action planner

10&11

Me & looking after myself

1 Coping with my changing body. Changing from being a girl to being a woman, and from being a boy to being a man. What is happening to my body? What changes will happen on the outside, and on the inside of my body? What do I need to know about these changes, and about human reproduction? What words should I use to talk about these changes? Are they *my* words?

2 How do the substances I put into my body affect how I feel? How do they affect how healthy I am now and in the future? I need to learn about what goes on inside my body. I need to learn about the substances I take into my body, including food and drink, inhalants, prescribed medicines, drugs and injections.

3 What do I need to know about smoking, alcohol, tea, coffee, inhalants and mood-changing substances?

4 How do I think my heart works and stays healthy? What effect do exercise, rest, sleep, smoke, inactivity and overeating have on my heart?

5 What happens when I'm ill? How does my body react and cope with being ill? What are the substances inside me which protect me from illness? How do I protect the 'protectors'? What can drugs do to me? What can I do to prevent myself becoming ill and to help myself to get better? How much of this is *my* responsibility? Who can I ask for help, advice and information?

6 Looking at lifestyles. How do I describe and judge lifestyles? What is the difference between real and fantasy lifestyles? Does image really matter? What image do I want to present?

7 Becoming and staying healthy. How do sleep, rest, fresh air and personal hygiene affect how healthy I am?

8 How does growing up increase my responsibilities? What are these responsibilities? How can I prepare for them? What do I need to know?

9 Exercise and enjoyment. Why do I need to exercise? How does it help my body, and the way that I feel?

10 How can I make best use of my leisure time? What leisure facilities are there around here? How do these help to promote health?

11 What kind of lifestyle do I think I have? What's best for me? Can I make healthy choices and change my lifestyle? How can I do this? Who will help me? Who can I learn from? How can I distinguish between fact, opinion and myth?

12 What happens to us when we live dangerously, or carelessly? What are the health hazards for me, and for other people? Who keeps me safe? What should I be kept safe from? What is *my* job?

13 What do I need to know:
- about diet, dieting, food, overeating and healthy eating?
- about body systems and the effect on them of the substances that enter my body?
- about enjoying my food, choosing my food, feeling good and other people's feelings about food?

What are the words I need to know to talk about:

- sex and sexuality in a public and private way?

- change, growing up and adult life?

- hazards?

- the problems I need help with?

Classroom strategies and activities for ages 10 and 11

● **Key themes**

The following pages describe in detail activities related to four key themes for this age group:

Themes	Content boxes	
Lifestyles and cultures	(16)→(6)→(31)	(see page 121)
Bullies (including coping strategies and relationships)	(22)→(36)	(see page 137)
Growing up (including relationships, responsibility and body changes)	(1)→(24)→(26)	(see page 145)
Substance abuse	(3)→(19)	(see page 165)

It is important that you select and modify these activities according to your needs. If you are devising your own health education programme you may be well aware of the health education priorities of your school, and may have selected the key themes you wish to explore with your pupils. If this is the case, you may find that the following activities are useful examples. On the other hand you may wish to incorporate them as they stand in your programme.

All the themes are explored through the content boxes which act as starting points for the activities. There are two other key themes relevant to this age group for which you may wish to plan your own activities:

Themes	Content boxes
Healthy eating	②→⑬→㊴
Keeping safe*	㉗→㊱→⑲→⑫

(A summary of the main strategies and activities used in this chapter can be found on page 172).

(*Additional material provided in *Health for Life 2*, see Appendix 2, page 186).

Theme ● *Lifestyles and cultures*

Use content boxes 16, 6 and 31:

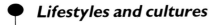

16

How can I value myself? How do people show that they value me? How can I show that I value other people's time, space, bodies, traditions, beliefs, feelings, privacy and possessions?

→

6

Looking at lifestyles. How do I describe and judge lifestyles? What is the difference between real and fantasy lifestyles? Does image really matter? What image do I want to present?

→

31

How do other people's lifestyles differ from mine? In what ways is growing up different for them? How can we get to know each other better? How can we work together to promote health? How can we help to prevent all kinds of discrimination?

This theme provides opportunities to explore:

- cultural and ethnic differences.
- getting on with people.
- specific aspects of discrimination.
- respect for self and others.

Lifestyles and cultures

16 **How can I value myself? How do people show that they value me? How can I show that I value other people's time, space, bodies, traditions, beliefs, feelings, privacy and possessions?**

Activity 1 ● *Why should I value myself?*

- Designing a coat of arms, discussion and sharing personal views.

- Individual activity followed by pair or small group activities, with an opportunity for family work.

You can start this activity by explaining to the children what is meant by a coat of arms – use historical material or literature to help you.

Invite the children to design individually their own coat of arms. Suggest that they incorporate illustrations of four different aspects of their lifestyles: appearance, interests, strengths and special relationships.

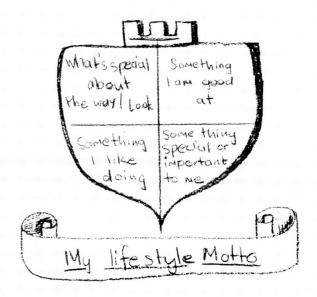

You could suggest to the children that they choose a motto to accompany their coat of arms. Explain to them how mottos express rules for sensible behaviour which are adopted by people (or institutions) and that they can sum up a person's lifestyle and attitudes. Look at some examples of mottos with the children and help them to develop their own personal versions.

Invite the children to look at each others' unnamed designs to see if they can tell to whom each one belongs.

Talk with them about the common elements in their designs, but emphasise that each coat of arms, and the person it represents, is unique.

Invite the children to display their work and explain their coats of arms to each other. Emphasise how important it is to know and understand oneself, and to value, appreciate and be proud of, oneself.

The children could, with your help, make a class, or group, coat of arms to illustrate their health interests or healthy lifestyle.

Family work: they could take home their individual coats of arms and explain them to their families.

There are **cross-curricular links** with:

— literature.

— history.

— geography.

— religious education.

Activity 2 ● *How do people show they value me?*

- Exploring the language associated with being valued. Discussion and generalisation. Writing and illustration.
- Individual and small group activities.

You could start by revising the work on coats of arms and valuing ourselves, emphasising that each of us is unique.

Invite the children to think of words and phrases which express what it feels like to be valued. Write these in the form of a 'circle of feelings' or a word box on the blackboard.

124

Ask the children to work either in pairs, or in small groups, or individually, and think of responses to the question 'What do people do to make you feel valued?' Initially their responses are likely to refer to specific occasions and people.

Invite the children to illustrate, and write about, their own experiences of being valued.

Bring all the children together to share their ideas and generalise about the kinds of activities which make people feel valued. Either, ask them to write these down, or, write them up on a blackboard or a large piece of paper yourself.

Talk with the children about how some of these valuing activities can be incorporated in day-to-day classroom life.

There are **cross-curricular links** with role-playing, mime and drama.

- Discussion in small groups. Extending children's vocabulary.

- Writing activity in small groups, with the teacher being a 'scribe' when necessary. This will provide the opportunity for one-to-one sharing.

Invite the children to recall the previous activity. Ask them to get into small groups and talk about what upsets them and makes them feel less valued. If this is sensitively handled, children will be able to put into words some of their feelings about the way adults and peers fail to respect them. It can be useful, for them and for you, to see some of these feelings expressed in writing. If some children still find writing difficult, you can write for them. This will provide an opportunity for some children to share personal problems with you.

Once children have thought about what upsets *them*, they should be able to suggest, and write down, ways in which they can value and respect other people.

What upsets me?

People who keep bothering me won't leave me alone, when people push me about, when I don't feel like being touched

People who want to know what I'm doing, where I'm going all the time

People who won't listen

People who treat me like a baby

People who tease people who call me names people who say I'm fat or stupid

Activity 4 ● *How can I show other people that I value them? (Role-play)*

- Role-playing, followed by discussion.

- Small group and shared activities.

Invite the children to plan and enact a role-play situation in which two children are 'ganging up' on another, for example, refusing to let her or him join in, teasing, tormenting or taking some possession away.

Ask the children to suggest the kinds of answers which the unkind children might give if another person came along and accused them of being unkind or uncaring.

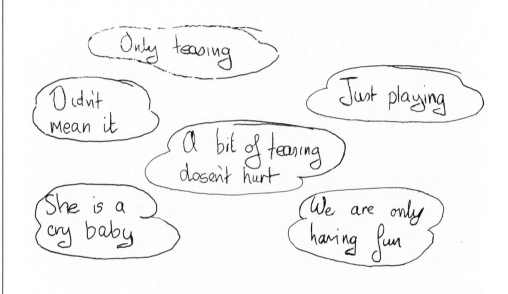

Write up some of the children's responses. Ask them if these are truthful answers.

Invite the children to put themselves in the place of the child who is being tormented and to imagine their feelings. Ask them to think of words to describe these feelings, for example, scared, bullied, lonely, worried, not valued. What might the child be saying and thinking? Can you say one thing and be thinking and feeling something else?

Ask the children to talk about the ways in which they could help the child who is being teased, and to consider the different outcomes. Invite them to plan, and enact, role-plays based on this situation. Come together to talk about how the teased child might have helped him or herself. The role-play could be presented by groups to the rest of the class and used later as a theme for art activities.

Look again at the chart in Activity 2 'How people make us feel valued'. Can the children pick out one or more ways which they could put into practice with their friends and families?

During these activities you could focus on a particular aspect of discrimination and disability which relates to your school or your class.

Lifestyles and cultures

6 **Looking at lifestyles. How do I describe and judge lifestyles? What is the difference between real and fantasy lifestyles? Does image really matter? What image do I want to present?**

Activity 1 ● *Lifestyles – the way we live*

- Discussion or brainstorming session. Devising a checklist or questionnaire which can be used to investigate a lifestyle.

- Class or group activity, with an opportunity for family work.

Talk with the children and invite them to imagine that they have been asked to describe someone's lifestyle. Encourage them to suggest some of the questions they would need to ask in order to form a complete picture, and to decide whether or not it was a healthy lifestyle. Make a list of their suggestions.

Invite the children to get into pairs or small groups, and put the list into some order. By the end of the session, each pair or group should have their own Healthy Lifestyles Checklist.

We want to find out :—

- What they eat and drink.
- What they do in their spare time.
- What they believe in.
- How they behave.
- Where they go and who with.
- How they look after themselves.
- How they get on with people.
- How they cope.
- If they are happy.
- The kind of friends they have.
- What they wear.
- What they know about being healthy.
- How much they exercise.
- If they smoke, drink, use drugs.

Bring the children together and encourage them to compare their lists. They might enjoy using their checklists like questionnaires and trying them out on each other.

128

You could summarise for the children the things which need to be considered when evaluating or understanding a lifestyle:

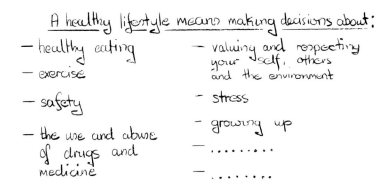

A healthy lifestyle means making decisions about:
— healthy eating
— exercise
— safety
— the use and abuse of drugs and medicine
— valuing and respecting your self, others and the environment
— stress
— growing up
— ....
— ....

Invite the children to think about how much, or how little, they know about these topics and to select those which they would like to explore further in groups or as a class.

Activity 2 ● *Healthy lifestyles*

- This is a fun exercise which will enable the children to consider, and evaluate, both their own and others' lifestyles.

- Class, group and individual activities with the opportunity for family work.

Invite the children to evaluate the lifestyle of an imaginary person, 'Crumbo', the lead singer of a group called 'The Crumbles', who leads a high risk, unhealthy life. Talk with the children about the kind of lifestyle led by the singer. Invite them to add to these descriptions:

smokes 40 cigarettes a day

lives on junk food especially cream cakes and chips

never eats breakfast

drinks 5 pints of beer a day

doesn't exercise

spends a lot of time on the road

is safety conscious about his equipment

spends a lot of time and money on his appearance

gets on with his group but worries about staying in the charts

CRUMBO

Ask the children to use their checklist and healthy lifestyle summary to evaluate this lifestyle. How would they rate it? Excellent? Good? Not bad? Poor? Very risky? Draw a rating guide for the children to fill in.

The healthy lifestyle rating for Crumbo	
	excellent
	good
	not bad
	poor
	very risky
Tick one box	

Ask the children to suggest some changes that 'Crumbo' could make.

Remind the children that this is an imaginary lifestyle. Invite them to assess the healthy or not so healthy lifestyles of some *real* people they know, or know about, for example, a long-distance lorry driver, a newsagent, a farm worker, an unemployed person or a person at home looking after a family. Ask them to use their checklist, summary and rating guide, and to write about and illustrate their results.

You could make a classroom display of the children's evaluations, paintings, drawings, and books about lifestyles and health.

Activity 3 ● ***What about my lifestyle?***

- Encourage the children to evaluate their own lifestyles using the checklists and rating guide from Activity 2.
- Individual or pair activity with an opportunity for family work.

Invite the children to think back to the work they did in the previous activity.

Ask them to work individually, or in pairs, and look at their own lifestyles with the checklists and summary, and fill in their rating guides.

This is my healthy lifestyle now

- I have lots of pals
- I don't worry much
- I go swimming
- I don't always get on with my mum
- I eat sensibly most days

My rating
— excellent
— good
— not bad ✓
— poor
— very risky

In what ways do they think they should change their lifestyle to make it healthier?

- This is the healthy lifestyle I would like
- These are the changes I would like to make: • ....
  - • ....
  - • ....
- I think .... would help me
- I am going to start with ....
  ....
  ....

Family work: the children could talk with their families about their lifestyles and their proposed improvements, and ask for their support.

Activity 4 ● *Images of me*

- Making an individual book or file about self-image.
- Individual activity with opportunities for sharing, discussion and family work.

Talk with the children about how they see themselves. Encourage them to concentrate on their personalities and characters rather than on their appearance. Make a note of useful words and phrases which describe different personalities.

Word box
quiet and gentle   cheerful
friendly
always around   happy
shy   loyal   bossy
unreliable   the worrying kind

Invite the children to write about and illustrate these themes: 'This is how I see myself . . .' and 'I think I am . . .'

Talk with them about how other people see us, for example, sometimes people still treat us like children even though we're growing up.

Invite the children to write about and illustrate themselves as other people see them, and to compare notes with other children. They could start by thinking about themes such as:

— How does my Mum (or another member of the family) see me?

— How does my teacher see me?

— How do my friends see me?

Encourage them to include their good points (children can be very hard on themselves when doing this kind of activity).

Suggest that they now repeat the exercise, this time using drawing and writing to illustrate: 'How would I like to be'. Invite the children to go through their work and pick out some change they believe they could make. Who or what would help them?

Ask the children to put all their work on image into individual books or files. They can add to these in many ways, for example, they could paste in photographs or drawings of themselves (at different ages) and of their families.

Family work: the children could take home their books or files, show them to their families and ask them for contributions.

Lifestyles and cultures

31 **How do other people's lifestyles differ from mine? In what ways is growing up different for them? How can we get to know each other better? How can we work together to promote health? How can we help to prevent all kinds of discrimination?**

Activity 1 ● *Other people's lifestyles*

- Setting up an 'agency' for putting children in touch with others with different lifestyles. Designing a questionnaire. Talking about the problems involved.

- Class or small group activity.

Suggest to the class that they set up an agency called 'Link Up', which will put children in touch with others with different lifestyles.

Tell them that the children who apply to the agency will be sent a lifestyle questionnaire. Ask the children to think about the kinds of questions it would be possible, or fair, to ask. Discuss this with them, or hold a brainstorming session, and make a note of their responses.

Ask the children to group these questions: which of them relate to person, place, personality, family etc? Which questions are concerned with *facts*? Which questions are concerned with *opinions*?

Ask the children if there are some questions which they would not ask or wouldn't like to be asked. Would they include questions about religion? race? parents? Would they ask if the people were disabled?

This is a good opportunity to explore attitudes, stereotypes, discrimination and anti-discriminatory policies.

```
           LIFESTYLES QUESTIONNAIRE

Name.............................................

Address..........................................

        .........................................

Age...............      Any family?..............

What do you look like?...........................

What are you interested in?......................

What special times do you celebrate?.............

What kind of person are you?.....................

What are you good at?............................

Where do you go to school?.......................

What friends do you have?........................

What do you like to eat?.........................

Do you like to exercise?.........................
```

Invite the children to work in small groups and to produce a simple questionnaire. Remind them that they are trying to get a picture of a person's lifestyle. When the questionnaires are finished the groups could exchange them, try completing them and evaluate them for each other.

Activity 2 ● *Getting to know you*

- Discuss the ways in which two children who have been linked up by the agency could get to know and understand each other better.

- This could be the basis of a variety of group and individual activities.

Remind the class that the 'Link Up' agency is now established. Children have been paired and addresses exchanged.

Ask the class what advice they would give to these pairs of children to help them to get to know each other better? What might these children ask? send? do? find out about?

Write up their responses so the children can choose which activities they would like to explore further.

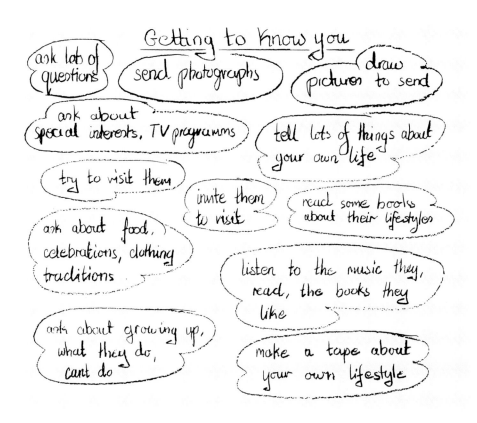

As you can see from the illustration above there are opportunities to incorporate letter writing, reading, illustration, making tapes, and other activities.

A 'link up' could be organised between your class and a class from a different area.

There are **cross-curricular links** with:

- environmental studies.
- religious education.
- literature.
- drama.
- music.

Activity 3 ● *Looking at attitudes*

- Exploring stereotypes and stereotyping, using discussion, pictures cut from magazines, writing and drawing.

- Class, group and individual activities.

Provide the children with the 'Link up' questionnaires of two fictitious people: Sammy and Jo. Include some information which might lead some children to make stereotyped judgements, for example:

— *Sammy* is 11, the youngest of a big family, likes ballet, drawing, playing with friends and cooking.

— *Jo* is 10, the middle child, likes sports, especially swimming and cycling, goes camping and hates getting dressed up.

Ask the children to add to these descriptions, and say whether they think Sammy and Jo are male or female and what kind of people they would expect them to be. Question any stereotyping which shows in their responses. Ask them to explain why we think that way.

Ask the children to draw and label stereotype characters, for example:

— a teenager	— a family
— a stranger	— a grandmother
— a doctor	— a kind person
— a nurse	— a cruel person
— a criminal	

Ask them to give examples of set attitudes concerning age, race, colour, sex and appearance.

Invite the children to look for and cut out pictures of stereotypes from comics, newspapers and magazines. Encourage them to question these stereotypes, for example,

— How are teachers depicted? Do they really look like that?

— How are 'goodies' and 'baddies' depicted? Do they really look like that?

Ask the children to collect pictures of faces, study them and give you their immediate impression or snap-judgement. Question these impressions and emphasise how important it is to know people, and know the facts, instead of jumping to conclusions. Invite them to work in groups and write about the faces and display their work on a wall chart.

You might think this person is bad but she could be sad

You might think he is happy but he might be a baddie

Lots of people thought she was beautiful but she is unhappy

What do you think of this person?

If you didn't stop and think you would say he was silly

Jumping to conclusions

You can extend these activities in order to focus on specific attitudes and aspects of stereotyping and discrimination which are relevant to your pupils.

Theme ● *Bullies (including coping strategies and relationships)*

Use content boxes 22 and 36:

22

What can I do when I'm frightened? lost? bullied? upset? under pressure? being persuaded? How can I help myself? Knowing how and when to say 'No', 'Give me time', 'Don't bully me', 'Why do you do that?', 'Let me decide'. Who can help me?

36

How do I decide which places are safe for me? Which places should I go to with friends or my family? How do I decide about strangers? How can I tell which people, places and situations are safe, and which are risky?

This theme provides opportunities to explore:

● what it feels like to be pressured and afraid.

● dealing with fear and pressure.

● different aspects of personal safety, such as child abuse.

Bullies (coping strategies and relationships)

 What can I do when I'm frightened? lost? bullied? upset? under pressure? being persuaded? How can I help myself? Knowing how and when to say: 'No', 'Give me time', 'Don't bully me', 'Why do you do that?', 'Let me decide'. Who can help me?

Activity 1 ● *What are we afraid of?*

- Organising a survey. Analysing the results. Discussion.
- Class, group and individual activities.

Invite the children to take part in a survey: 'What are we afraid of?' (You could contribute to the survey too.)

Provide slips of paper. Ask the children to write one thing that frightens them on each slip, it could be a situation, a person, or a place. Encourage them to complete as many slips as possible, keeping them unsigned.

Important: this exercise could provide a child with his or her first opportunity to reveal some personal distress or sensitivity.

Ask the children to suggest ways of classifying the responses, and to help you sort the slips of paper according to category. Either you or the children could count how many slips there are in each category, and display the results on a chart like this one.

<u>Imaginary fears</u>

Fears about what <u>might happen</u>
✓✓✓✓

Fears about what is happening
✓✓

Fears about <u>people</u>
✓✓

Fears about <u>myself</u>
✓✓✓✓✓✓✓

Fears about <u>places</u>
✓✓✓

Fears about <u>accidents</u>
✓✓✓✓

Fears about <u>things, noises</u> etc.
✓✓✓✓

Talk about the results with the children. Invite them to share some of their experiences, to talk about their fears of imaginary things and to explain why they have fears about themselves – are these concerned with their physical development or their relationships?

Invite the children to share with others their own ways of coping with different kinds of fear. Their responses may be very specific, but at this stage they will, with some help, be able to generalise and develop these specific answers into strategies. Enlarge the children's range of strategies if necessary.

What helps us cope when we are afraid?

We stay with friends

We find someone to tell, to share with

We keep away from the crowd

We pray

We talk to ourselves and say *don't be silly*

We run away

We face up to it

We phone for help

We sing and whistle

Ask the children to look for strategies which contradict each other, for example, 'Stay with friends' and 'Keep away from the crowd'. Encourage them to explore these and suggest times when they might use one and not the other.

Ask them to think about which strategies are appropriate for specific situations such as, when one is being bullied, being pestered, being alone.

Encourage them to distinguish between the strategies which make them feel better and those which solve the problem, or keep them safe.

Activity 2 ● *Dealing with bullies and bullying*

- Learning about feelings through language, discussion, role-play planning and role-playing.

- Class or group activity with opportunities for individual follow-up work and family involvement.

You could use as your starting point a poem (for example *First Day at School* by Roger McGough), a story or an extract from a story, to set the scene for a discussion about playground fears or problems in the classroom.

rushing about   being left out

clamour   being made to do things,

noise, shouting   nowhere to go

gangs plotting   words I don't understand

Invite the children as a class to share in the making of a word picture of a noisy, frightening playground scene. Invite them to think of words and phrases for sounds, movement, the feelings of those who enjoy the clamour and bustle, and the feelings of those who don't enjoy it.

In smaller groups, or as pairs, invite the children to complete:

— a set of speech bubbles which contain snatches of conversation from the playground scene, and/or

— a set of thought bubbles which capture what people are thinking but not saying.

Ask the groups to share what they have written.

Talk with the children and ask them to think of ways of coping with bullies. What can they do? What can they say? How do we tackle bullying? Is all playground roughness bullying? Do bullies know what they are doing and how they are making people feel? How can we teach them? Would role-playing help?

Explore the question 'How can we help ourselves?' Responses might include 'Fight back', 'Stand up to them', 'Avoid the places where they go', 'Don't show you're afraid', 'Look and sound confident', 'Stay with friends', 'Think ahead', 'Learn from last time', 'Share the problem with a friend or trusted adult', 'Practice saying "No" or "Go away"', 'Ignore them', 'Don't think it's your fault'.

Encourage the children to explore these coping strategies and to think of times when they would be useful, and times when they would not be so useful.

Invite the children to work in groups and develop role-play situations in which children learn to cope with bullying. Ask them to write down the role-plays in the form of playlets, clearly setting out the dialogue, the action and the characters. Encourage them to invent alternative endings. You could use these playlets to provide other children with practice in using coping strategies.

Crowd scenes can provide an exciting theme for art work which can be explored using a variety of media, and for shared and individual creative writing. There is a wealth of literature which explores becoming stronger and more self-confident, and which deals with pressure, teasing and bullying.

Children who are being bullied may sometimes feel ashamed that they have allowed themselves to get into this situation, or to be so easily upset. Others may be unwilling to share the problem with you, or other adults, for fear of being accused of telling tales.

Some children may feel that they are bullied because of some physical shortcoming or disability and that since they cannot change this, they cannot change their strategies for dealing with the problem.

You and the children may want to discuss these problems, alternatively, you could suggest them as themes for role-playing.

Some children, even in a very open classroom, may be sensitive about revealing their feelings and fears to other children, particularly if the bullied and the bullies are in the same class. It may be that small group activities would best support their needs.

Discussing the question: 'Who can help me?' with the children might provide an opportunity for them to look beyond the school and its pressures to the work of groups in the community who provide support for families and for children, especially those who provide a confidential listening service. These will vary with each community, but might, for example, include The Samaritans and Childline.

There are **cross-curricular links** with:

- topic work on the community.
- moral and religious education.
- visits and visitors.
- environmental studies.

Bullies (coping strategies and relationships)

 How do I decide which places are safe for me? Which places should I go to with friends or my family? How do I decide about strangers? How can I tell which people, places and situations are safe, and which are risky?

Activity 1 ● *How do I decide which places are safe for me?*

- Discussing or brainstorming. Summarising. Writing and drawing. Planning, writing and acting role-plays.

- Class or group activities.

Hold a brainstorming session with the class, or with smaller groups in which the children think of all the places they go to (apart from school and home). Ask each child to make a list of these places, for example:

- youth clubs

- discos

- the church

- the park

- playgrounds

- the streets

- other people's homes

- the leisure centre

- the woods

- the canal

- the cinema

- the town centre

- entertainment arcades

Invite the children to compare, and add to, their lists, and to talk about the places they think are safe to go to:

- alone;

- with friends;

- with family;

- with other known adults.

Ask them to group their list of places under the above headings, and explain what, in their view, makes a place safe or hazardous.

Ask the children to think about the hazards they might encounter at these places. Do these change according to the time or company? Does being aware of the hazards make places less dangerous?

Explore with the children:

— situations which are potentially hazardous;

— ways in which these situations might be avoided;

— ways of coping if the situation becomes difficult.

Think about, and make a list of, coping strategies and practise these through role-play. Focus on strategies for saying 'No', for finding support, and avoiding involvement.

This could be a good opportunity to look at strategies which children can use to cope with people known to them who become, or appear to be becoming, a hazard or danger, for example:

— peers, who were once friends but are now posing a threat;

— different levels of child abuse;

— being pressurised by peers to take part in substance abuse, vandalism, violence or sexual activity.

Ask the children to work in small groups and to plan, write and act out role-plays based on these situations. It is easier for some children to plan or write a role-play for others to perform than to take part in the performance itself, especially when they may have reason to be distressed about this sort of situation.

Safe and unsafe places could be a theme for creative activities, such as making a wall story or poster display. Before the children begin, ask them to specify which messages they want to put across with their pictures, and to use speech bubbles, thought bubbles or mottos to reinforce these messages.

Activity 2 ● *How can I tell which places are safe and which are risky?*

● Devising and using a 'risk scale'. Learning how to minimise risk.

● Class, group and individual activities.

Risk scale

0. safe _ _ _

1 very low risk _ _ _

2. low risk _ _ _

3. risky _ _ _

4. very risky _ _ _

5. dangerous _ _ _

Provide the children with copies of a risk scale like the one below or invite them to work in groups to devise their own.

Invite them, individually or in pairs, to list the places they have been to during the last week, including home and school, and to evaluate each place using their risk scale.

Ask them to set out the results as a table, showing the degree of risk taken in each case. Invite them to compare their results and to discuss how they might have tried to, or did try to, minimise the risk. Would these places have been *more* or *less* risky if they had gone alone? Or if they had gone with friends? Or if they had gone with a stranger? You could invite the children to explore this further using writing and illustration.

Invite the children to devise comic strip cartoons which illustrate these risks. Ask them to show clearly the characters, the type of situation and to provide two alternative endings – one good and one not so good.

Ask the children to pinpoint the critical moment in their comic strip situations, when the story could have gone in either direction. Ask them to look at what was said or done which decided the way the story ended. The skill of finding the critical moment can be practised using literature, drama and movement. It is a skill which children can be asked to use when they have problems with relationships at home or at school.

Theme *Growing up (including relationships, responsibility and body changes)*

Use content boxes 1, 24 and 26:

1

Coping with my changing body. Changing from being a girl to being a woman, and from being a boy to being a man. What is happening to my body? What changes will happen on the outside, and on the inside, of my body? What do I need to know about these changes, and about human reproduction? What words should I use to talk about these changes? Are they *my* words?

→

24

What does it mean to be grown-up? What is involved in growing-up? How do I feel about the changes in my body, and in others' bodies? Do I want to hurry this growing-up process? What words should I use to tell, and ask, people about these changes? Who can I ask for help?

→

26

Does growing up mean taking on more responsibility? How can I be responsible for my body, my feelings and for what happens to me? How can I cope with my own and other people's emotions: love, loss hate, envy, despair, separation, birth, death, grief, comfort, conflict, unease. How do I feel about my own and others' sexuality?

This theme provides opportunities to explore:

- physical changes.

- human reproduction.

- sexuality and feelings.

Growing up

Coping with my changing body. Changing from being a girl to being a woman, and from being a boy to being a man. What is happening to my body? What changes will happen on the outside, and on the inside, of my body? What do I need to know about these changes, and about human reproduction? What words should I use to talk about these changes? Are they *my* words?

This theme provides a framework on which you can base sex education. Under the Education (No.2) Act 1986, the governors of schools are responsible for deciding whether sex education should be given in their schools and in what form. Schools are advised to familiarise themselves with this Act and with the subsequent DES Circular 11/87 (Welsh Office 45/87) 'Sex Education at School'.

The following activities build on work done in the earlier age ranges, and provide children with opportunities to clarify what they know, and learn more. You can either deal with sensitive issues as they arise or build them into the framework.

It is important to remember that most children are presented with images of sex everyday from television, newspapers, magazines, popular music, and advertising which have little to do with reality. They have to come to terms with this while learning from the activities you organise for them.

Activity 1 • *Lifelines*

- Designing an illustrated 'lifeline' running from pre-birth to old age. Talking together about adolescence and summarising information.
- Individual and group activity with the opportunity for family involvement.

Invite the children to help you to construct a 'lifeline' chart which illustrates the stages we pass through from conception to old age.

Ask the children to think about growth – its speed and variations – and to summarise their view of each stage on the chart.

Encourage the children to identify the time of greatest change for them.

Invite them to look at the range of body sizes and shapes within the class, within other classes and their families.

Growing and Children's lifeline

Unborn	Babies	Children	Adolescents	Grown ups	Older people
A baby grows slowly in its mum	Babies grow and change quickly	Children's bodies grow and change at all different times	Big changes happen inside and out	Grown ups don't change much they get fatter or thinner	Some old people get smaller and bent

My idea of a growing and changing life. Fred

Focus on:

- growth spurts;

- the influence of heredity;

- the unique pattern of each child's growth and development;

- adolescence as a time of great change. Emphasise that each child moves through this stage at their own pace.

Important: children at this age can differ greatly in their rates of growth and development. Some may be physically very advanced, while others may not appear to be changing or growing much. This can produce worries and it is important to reassure the children that these differences are normal, and that each individual has an in-built 'time clock' (except in very rare cases where growth has been inhibited by a medical condition).

Activity 2 ● *My changing body*

- Designing a personal 'lifeline'.
- Individual activity with opportunities for sharing and family work.

Invite the children to devise their own lifelines which pin-point changes in their growth. They could illustrate these with their own drawings or with photographs from home.

My growing and changing lifeline —					
0-1 years	1-4 years	4-7 years	7-8 years	8-9 years	NOW
My mum had me in hospital I weighed 6lb 2oz thats small.	I grew very fast I could walk when I was ①	I was one of the smallest in the class when I started school.	I started to shoot up I was very skinny	I was the tallest in the class	I'm average now but still skinny I am changing a lot from a girl to a woman.

Invite the children to compare their lifelines, talk about them and display them. Emphasise the fact that while all the lifelines have features, each one is unique.

Family work: the children could ask their families about:

- their weight at birth;
- landmarks in their growth and development as recalled by older members of the family;
- recent significant changes.

This family work could provide a useful starting point for a holistic programme of sex education which would reassure the families that a broad-based approach was being used.

Activity 3 ● *Changing from being a boy to being a man, and from being a girl to being a woman.*

- Discussion. Exploring the personal and public language associated with puberty, growth and reproduction.
- Group and family work.

Talk about the last box on the children's personal lifeline charts and explore the physiological changes which take place as boys and girls become men and women. Discuss how these changes relate to the ability to conceive and have children.

Outline the different changes for boys and girls:

Girls	Boys
Sweat glands become more active	Sweat glands become more active
Breasts develop	Penis and testicles grow
Hips widen	Voice breaks
Body hair grows	Body hair grows
Menstruation begins	

You will need to introduce the children to the formal or public language used to describe physiological development, and to explore with them the difference between this and the private language of home, street and playground. Children need to be able to recognise both as they appear in print and conversation.

Some useful formal or public words you may want to introduce:

pubic	ovaries
menstruation	puberty
penis	periods
vagina	cycle
discharge	testicles
reproduction	semen
enlarge	preparation

Activity 4 ● *Coping with the changes*

- Discussing coping strategies, with opportunities for writing and illustration.
- Small group and individual activities with an opportunity for family work.

Focus on the changes which the children have outlined in their personal lifelines, for example, going to school, changing class or school, having a new brother or sister and no longer being the only one or the youngest. Ask them to recall how they felt. Encourage them to see that for many people change is both frightening and exciting, and that changes at puberty are particularly so.

Growing Up

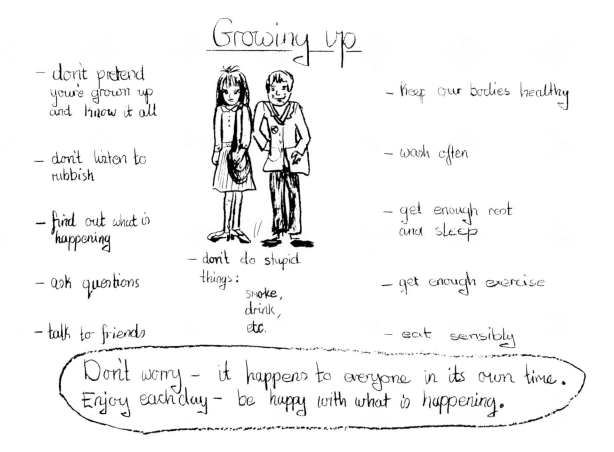

- don't pretend you're grown up and know it all

- don't listen to rubbish

- find out what is happening

- ask questions

- talk to friends

- don't do stupid things: smoke, drink, etc.

- keep our bodies healthy

- wash often

- get enough rest and sleep

- get enough exercise

- eat sensibly

Don't worry — it happens to everyone in its own time. Enjoy each day — be happy with what is happening.

Invite the children to think of ways in which they can cope with these changes. Suggest that they first concentrate on their bodies and then on their feelings. Display and add to their suggestions.

Encourage the children to talk about their experiences of trying these strategies. What were the outcomes? What problems did they meet? Were these to do with relationships, or language, or lack of information?

Invite the children to express some of these experiences through writing and drawing or painting. This is an opportunity for role-play, which will enable the children to practise strategies and discuss them.

It might be useful to start a special collection of:
- books and pamphlets about physiological changes,
- literature which has as its theme aspects of adolescence.

Invite the children to make an index and/or catalogue of these materials and to look for material to add to the collection, for example, magazine articles, teenage comics, letters to 'agony aunts'.

The children might like to write their own problem pages, working in groups to prepare both problems and replies.

Growing up

24 **What does it mean to be grown-up? What is involved in growing up? How do I feel about the changes in my body, and in others' bodies? Do I want to hurry this growing up process? What words should I use to tell, and ask, people about these changes? Who can I ask for help?**

Activity I ● *What is involved in growing-up?*

- Analysing the stages of growth and growing older. Sorting and grouping ideas. Extending vocabulary.

- Class, group and individual activities with the opportunity for family work.

With the children, make a collection of pictures of people of all ages from magazines and newspapers. Invite the children to work in groups and use these pictures to illustrate a lifeline which shows all the stages in life from pregnancy to old age.

Invite the groups to talk about what they mean by being grown-up. When are people grown-up? What characterises each age range? When are people old? When are they middle-aged?

Make a list of words, or write a 'word box' for the blackboard with all the vocabulary which relates to the different stages in life. Encourage children to add to this list as the work progresses. For example:

foetus	top class	adults
pregnancy	newcomers	senior citizens
infant	first years	grown-ups
baby	leavers	old-age pensioners
toddler	teenagers	elders
newborn	teens	elderly
kids	puberty	old folk
pre-school	adolescents	
juniors	parents	
seniors	youngsters	

Family work: invite the children to ask their families if they have special words for life stages and groups of people.

The children could ask their families to take part in a survey on views of age using questions such as:

'I think youth is from . . . to . . .'

'I think middle age is from . . . to . . .'

'I think old age is from . . . to . . .'

'I think being young means . . .'

'I think being grown-up means . . .'

Children could then compare the results of their family surveys.

Activity 2 ● *What does being grown-up mean?*

- Looking at the notion of being grown-up from two points of view, summarising and generalising.

- Class or group activities, with opportunities for individual and family work.

We think being grown up means:
- *being able to do what you like – be the boss*
- *having your own money*
- *having your own family*
- *having your own place*
- *finding a job*
- *looking after yourself*
- *being able to drive wear make up, stay out*

Continue with the theme of what the children and their families mean by growing up, and the differences in their views. Now focus on what being grown-up means to different people, inviting the children to offer their views first. Invite them to work in groups and make a list of their views, entitled 'We think being grown-up means . . .' and illustrate it.

Family work: ask the children if they think grown-ups would agree with their list, then invite them to take their work home to share with their families.

Ask the children to find out their families' views on what it means to be 'grown-up', and to list them.

Ask the children to compare their views on being grown-up with that of their families, also it might be interesting for them to compare differing views among families.

Grown ups think grown up means . . . . .
- *having a lot of responsibility*
- *looking after other people*
- *paying bills*
- *worrying about things*
- *making new friends*
- *not having a job*
- *wanting a better job*
- *having a family*
- *having fun*
- *being loved, loving*

Explore with the children how people change and become grown-up. At what stage do they learn to:

— be responsible?   — manage money?

— care for a family?   — etc . . .

Invite the children to suggest ways in which they have already begun to acquire these skills and ways in which they could extend them.

Activity 3 ● *How do I feel about growing up?*

- Identifying the ways in which children's coping strategies have changed over the years. Observing and evaluating other people's coping strategies.

- Class, group, pair and individual activities, with opportunities for working in pairs and family work.

Invite the children to work in groups, in pairs or as a class and to think back to how they would have reacted to the same difficult situation at the age of 3, at the age of 6 and at the present time. Examples of difficult situations could include getting lost, being told they can't have something, being bullied or bothered by other people, having injections, or going out for the day with the family.

Invite the children to think about not only how differently they might have reacted when they were younger, but also about the underlying reasons for this, for example, fear, lack of skill, lack of knowledge, changing interests.

Invite the children to write about and illustrate some of these changing reactions and to write down their answers to the question: 'Why don't I do that anymore?' You could display this work or invite them to take it home and share it with their families who may be able to add other examples of changing reactions.

Encourage the children to relate the acquisition of the skills, information and interests which help them to cope with life to the process of growing up. Suggest that they become more skilled observers of the adults around them and note how they cope with difficult situations. You could share your own coping strategies with the children. Invite them to identify new strategies which they might use.

The development of coping strategies provides good material for role-play and art.

Activity 4 ● *How do I feel about growing up?*

- Language activity. Making a 'circle of feelings'. Discussion with opportunities for creative activity.

- Individual, pair, and group activities.

Provide, or ask the children to write and draw, a 'circle of feelings', with a small picture of themselves at the centre. Ask them to include words, phrases and pictures which describe how they feel about growing up. They could talk with each other about this before they begin writing. Emphasise that phrases are better than single words for expressing feelings.

looking forward
to it

depressed because
it's not happening
yet

wishing it
would hurry up

Impatient
can't wait

happy most of
the time

me

not too sure

thinking
about
growing up

a bit worried,
sometimes
in case I can't
cope

Suggest that it is possbile for us to feel differently about things from one day to the next and even experience contradictory feelings.

Invite the children to share and discuss their work in pairs or in small groups. Ask a group of children to help you look through the work and pick out the feelings which appear more or less frequently. Present these to the rest of the class as a table like the one below.

Our feelings about growing up :

most frequent

- happy ⑩
- a bit worried ④
- excited ⑧
- not too sure ③
- can't wait ⑥
- depressed ③
- impatient ⑤
- tired of waiting ①

least frequent

There are **cross-curricular links** with:

— literature.   — creative writing.   — art.

The more children can put their feelings into words or interpret them through artistic activities the more they will feel at ease with them.

It is important to emphasise the positive aspects of the feelings children have about changing and growing up, while providing opportunities for exploring areas of concern.

Activity 5 ● *When I'm grown-up I will . . .*

- Imagining and evaluating aspirations. Sorting and categorising. Distinguishing between reality and fantasy.

- Individual, group, and class activities. Family work.

Ask the children what they want to be when they grow up. You could use poems or stories as a starting point. Invite them to compare what they want to be now with what they wanted to be when they were younger.

Provide slips of paper and invite the children to write down all the things they want to be or to do, completing as many slips as they can.

Their responses may tend to focus on:

– fame or specific jobs, for example, nurse, pop star or sports personality.

– appearance, for example, tall, beautiful.

– skills, for example, clever, fit, healthy.

– feelings, for example, happy, loved.

– family status, for example, married, in love, having children.

– opportunities, for example, travel, wealth.

– possessions, for example, car, house.

It might help to prompt the children with questions such as: 'What about your health . . . your feelings?' etc.

Ask the children to get into groups, sort their slips of paper and summarise them, either verbally, pictorially or as a written piece. Ask them to come together as a class, compare results and discuss which ambitions are realistic or less realistic.

Suggest to the children that, in order to ensure that some of these goals and aspirations are achieved, they choose one which they can begin working towards immediately. They could do this individually or in pairs.

There are **cross-curricular links** with:

– topic work, especially topics related to the community and the roles adults play.

– media studies, for example, children could study television, including advertising, serials and situation comedies, music, teenage comics, magazines and newspapers to find out how adult life is presented. Families could be asked to support and contribute to this activity.

Activity 6 ● *What worries me?*

- Using a 'worry box' as a way of airing some of the children's concerns about puberty. Discussing and sorting ideas.

- Individual activity with opportunities for sharing.

While it is not a good idea to over-emphasise that puberty is a time for worry, this activity could be useful for dealing with children's fears and concerns. Make a 'worry box' with a slot in the lid into which the children can put notes about their concerns (they can do this anonymously if they wish).

There are several ways in which you could respond to these concerns:

— You could choose the concerns which were written about the most frequently, and talk about them to a group of children. Summarise the concerns in your own words, and invite them to comment or suggest answers, while you provide the factual information required.

— You could pick out a problem posed by one child only, but which you feel may be of concern to others, and explore that.

Another way of approaching a concern is to identify it. Is it:

— a real concern which can be removed by finding out the facts?

— a real concern which can be alleviated by sharing it with someone, and by trying some suggested coping strategies?

— a concern based on an 'old wives' tale', superstition, hearsay or playground gossip, which can be removed by being examined openly?

— groundless (though not unimportant) fears?

— concerns about which we can do something, starting now?

Activity 7 ● *Do I want to hurry this growing up process?*

● Comparing and contrasting the lifestyles of children who are trying to hurry growing up, with those who are letting the process take its course.

● Individual and shared activities, with an opportunity for family involvement.

Provide the children with, or ask them to write a description of, the lifestyles of a boy and a girl, who are both rushing into adult life. What kind of things might they be doing? saying? pretending? thinking? Are they successful at hurrying the growing up process?

<u>Jo's lifestyle</u>

She goes around with a much older crowd

She smokes (to keep up with them)

She has dates with boys

she says she isn't interested in dolls etc any more

She stays out late

She wears make up and very grown up outfits

<u>Sam's lifestyle</u>

He drinks, smokes & boasts.

He swears.

He goes around with a much older crowd.

He stays out late.

He wears the latest gear.

He thinks exercise is stupid.

He copies pop stars.

He boasts about the girls he takes out.

He says he's not interested in sports any more but likes being in a rough crowd at a match.

Invite them to evaluate these lifestyles in terms of health and of risk. Ask the children to talk about the advice they would give Jo and Sam. Categorise their advice under different headings, such as:

— risks to their present and future health

— risks to their safety

— risks to their happiness

— risks to their relationships with family and friends

Explore with the children the idea of letting the growing up process take its course and what this means and entails, for example:

— knowing about the changes in our bodies, why they are happening and how they prepare us for being an adult.

— knowing about the changes in our feelings, why they are happening, and how these prepare us for being an adult.

— knowing that each of us grows and matures at our own rate, and that trying to hurry this process by changing our outward behaviour before we are mature enough to cope with the consequences can cause problems.

There are **cross-curricular links** with:

— science.

— literature.

— media studies, in particular studying the portrayal of adolescence on television, in magazines etc.

Activity 8 ● *How can I help myself? Who can help me?*

● Discussing the effectiveness of different coping strategies. Using role-play to practise different strategies.

● Class and group activities.

Discuss with the children the ways in which they cope when they are worried. (You could contribute some of your own strategies.)

Make a note of the different strategies used. Discuss each one in terms of its effectiveness and its limitations, with the children's help summarise these different strategies on a chart similar to the one opposite.

Invite the children to suggest ways of approaching people with their problems. Make a note of them, and encourage the children to try them out using role-play. Invite them to evaluate each different method of opening such a conversation.

Remind children of the other coping strategies they have talked about in previous activities.

It helps

I can talk to friends   --But.. Sometimes they dont know any more than I do. Sometimes they boast or pretend they know and I feel worse

I can talk to my family   --But..   Sometimes I don't know how to start. I'm shy. I don't have the words. Sometimes they get embarrassed. Sometimes they haven't got time.

I can talk to the school nurse   --But..   She is not always here. When she's here she's busy. I'm not sure what to say.

I can look it up in a book   --But.. I don't understand the words.

I can talk to other adults   -But---   It's not easy to get them on their own. I don't know how to start.

I can keep telling myself it's all perfectly normal and happens to everyone   --But-. I still need some help.

Growing up

26 **Does growing-up mean taking on more responsibility? How can I be responsible for my body, my feelings and for what happens to me? How can I cope with my own and other people's emotions: love, loss, hate, envy, despair, separation, birth, death, grief, comfort, conflict, unease. How do I feel about my own and others' sexuality?**

Activity 1 ● *Taking on more responsibility*

- Discussing and writing about responsibility. Making decisions about personal responsibilities.

- Pair and small group activities, with an opportunity for family involvement.

Ask the children to think about all the things which adults are responsible for, and the things which children are responsible for, and to list them in two parallel columns which you can draw for them if necessary. They could work in pairs or small groups. They should produce something like this:

Grown ups are responsible for:	We are responsible for:
– paying taxes	– going to school
– passing laws	– working hard
– keeping places safe & clean	– looking after our belongings
– looking after people	– looking after younger children
– voting	– keeping ourselves clean
– being honest	– making decisions about our lifestyles
– setting an example	– making and keeping friends

Invite the children to share and discuss their lists.

Talk with the children and ask them to identify areas in which:

— they feel they cannot take on more responsibility.

— they would like to take on more responsibility, but feel it might not be permitted by their families or their teachers.

— they feel they are not yet ready for more responsibility.

Invite them to think of some minor, new responsibilities which they could start working on now. Suggest that they draw up a contract listing these responsibilities, which they could sign (or, you could write, or type, one for them to fill in). In addition, the children could ask a friend, or an adult they are close to, to agree to help them become more responsible. Either you, or the children, could draw up another contract for them to sign.

Family work: this is a good opportunity to involve families and get their support.

Contract

I would like to get to be more responsible
I think I could start with

....
....

I will ask .... to help me.
Signed ....

Child's contract

Contract

I will try and help

....

to be more responsible

....

Signed ....

Friend's contract

Write on the blackboard some vocabulary which might be useful for this activity, such as:

resolve

declare

plan

responsible

resolution

Activity 2 ● *How can I be responsible for my feelings?*

- Talking about situations in which the children lost control of their feelings. Language activity. Thinking of coping strategies.

- Individual and small group activities.

It is difficult for children to take on more responsibility for their feelings at a time when these are likely to be unstable. It is important, however, that the children do have the opportunity to talk about this, and to realise that such strong and fluctuating feelings are a normal part of growing up.

It may be helpful to start by encouraging children to talk about experiences in which they lost control of, or were in danger of losing control of, their feelings. Talk about how they felt, what they had done or said, and whether or not they wished that it could be undone or unsaid. A useful starting point might be to ask them to complete a sentence such as, 'I wish the floor could have opened up when I . . .'.

Invite the children to share this sort of experience with a partner, or a small group, or to write about and illustrate different aspects of it. Suggest that as part of this activity they make two circles of feeling: one to illustrate how they felt, and one to illustrate how they think the other person, or persons, involved felt.

Encourage the children to think of ways in which they could assert greater control over their feelings, and be more aware of the impact of their behaviour on others' feelings.

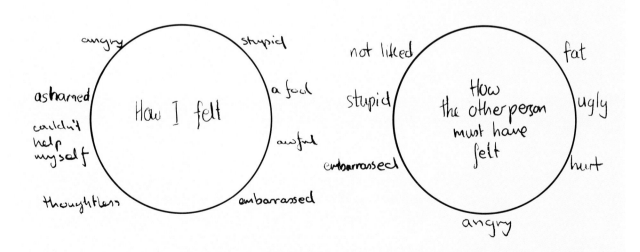

Activity 3 ● *Coping with love and changing feelings*

- Talking about the children's perceptions of love. Looking at words and phrases which help to illuminate these feelings.

- Small group activity.

You can find starting points in poetry, music, drama, literature, history and zoology for exploring children's perceptions of love.

Some children of this age will be experiencing feelings which they may interpret as 'being in love'. Others may have only experienced love as part of the family situation.

In small groups discuss the many aspects of love. Either you, or another member of the group, could make a note of the words and phrases which best express and encapsulate the children's views. There may be children for whom this discussion could be distressing or embarrassing and for whom a one-to-one talk may be more appropriate.

Talk with the children about how feelings can change quickly.

Provide the children with a range of words and phrases which express strong feelings. For each word or phrase, ask the children to find words which express opposite feelings or a range of opposite feelings.

Find the opposite feelings

love   hate
content
alone

starry eyed
on top of the world
no one understands
hopeless
trust
grief stricken
exhilaration

Invite the children to group these words into two circles of feeling, one for good feelings and the other for feelings which are not so good.

Invite the children to share with each other through talking, writing, drawing or role-playing, some of the times when they have experienced some of these feelings. You could share some of your own experiences with them.

Explore with the children the sources of these feelings, other than their own or others' behaviour, for example, music, films, stories, or poems which spark off strong emotions.

Talk with the children about differentiating between having feelings for people whom they know and having feelings for imaginary people or people of high status.

The word *fancy* ('I fancy him', 'She fancies me') is often used by children of this age to express aspects of sexuality. It may help to explore the other meanings of the word, for example, 'I *fancy* I would like that person', 'I *fancy* I would like to know that person better', 'I *fancy* that person would like me', 'I *fancy* we could have a (good) relationship'.

Encourage the children to explore, through talk, or role-play, the good and not so good feelings they have about themselves and the people they love, or feel they could love.

Loss of friendship, the breaking up of a loving boy–girl relationship and the death or absence of a family member can be very painful situations for children at this stage. They can find that sharing these feelings with others, and interpreting them through language and role-play is very reassuring.

Theme ● *Substance abuse*

Use content boxes 3 and 19:

3

19

What do I need to know about smoking, alcohol, tea, coffee, inhalants, and mood-changing substances?

⟶

Being aware of the pressures and influences on me, particularly those concerned with the substances I take into my body. Who, and what, can persuade me? When and how can I be persuaded? How can I learn to cope and make my own decisions?

This theme provides opportunities to explore:

● substances which can damage health or change behaviour.

● influences, pressures and strategies for recognising and coping with these.

Substance abuse

3 **What do I need to know about smoking, alcohol, tea, coffee, inhalants and mood-changing substances?**

This is a period when children may experiment with various substances. They may be pressured, concerned and misinformed and may not talk much about it. Activities which provide opportunities for them to share their experiences, clarify what they know, and find out the facts, are important.

Activity 1 ● ***What are the do's and don'ts of a healthy lifestyle?***

- Researching, recording and classifying information. Discussion.
- Group activity.

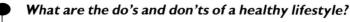

Dos 🙂   Don'ts ☹

Dos	Don'ts
exercise	worry, overwork
eat healthy food	smoke drink
get enough sleep	mess with
have breakfast	drugs
say where you're going	get dragged in
	get attacked
say NO	get fat

Invite the children to make a list of the do's and don'ts of a healthy lifestyle. You could ask them to contribute their own ideas, and the ideas of people at school and in the media. They could get information from posters, leaflets, newspaper headlines, magazine articles and television advertising.

Alternatively you could make an instant display of their spoken contributions, invite them to add to this over a period of several days, and then invite them to classify their contributions using the criteria 'Who says so?'

Suggest that the children examine the sources of this information, for example, television, doctor, family, school, government, friends. Ask them to think of the reasons why they think people say 'do' and 'don't'. Encourage them to ask: 'What might these people know that we don't yet know?'

Invite the children to select some health topics which they would like to know more about, for example: 'How does smoking affect my body?' Ask them to write the topics on slips of paper or as a list, and use them as the basis of the next activity.

Activity 2 ● *What do I need to know more about?*

- Identifying aspects of substance abuse on which the children want more information. Analysing and presenting the findings of a survey.

- Class and group activities, with an opportunity for family involvement.

I think I would like to know more about how

alcohol affects my body ... ☑

smoking affects my body ... ☐

tea and coffee affect my body ... ☐

drugs affect my body ... ☐

glue affects my body ... ☐

In order to find out which aspects of substance abuse the children want to know more about, you can either use the list of topics the children made during the last activity, or, offer them a list of topics, and ask them to select those in which they are interested.

You could organise this activity as a survey of the children's interest in different aspects of substance abuse. The children could devise their own ways of indicating the strength of their interest, and working in groups or as a class, they could help you to analyse and present the results.

You could ask families, health professionals and other members of the school community to contribute their expertise and support.

There are **cross-curricular links** with:
– mathematics (survey presentation and statistics) and media studies.

Activity 3 ● *What do I need to know about smoking?*

- Brainstorming and discussion. Tapping children's own perceptions. Extending information and pinpointing misinformation.

- Class, small group or paired activities with the opportunity for family involvement.

Group 3 what we'd like to know about smoking?

- Why do people smoke?
- Why is it hard to stop?
- Does it hurt if you smoke and then give up?
- Does it stop you growing?
- What can you do if people keep on at you to try?

- Why do they do it if it is bad for them?
- Will it hurt my mum if she goes on smoking?
- Why shouldn't you smoke if you're having a baby?

Sian, Sam, Billy Jo, Tamsin

Invite the children to work in pairs or small groups, and hold brainstorming sessions on what they want to know about smoking. Ask them to write down all the questions they would like to ask. Suggest they do not just think about the effects smoking has on their bodies, but that they could also look at wider concerns and questions.

Invite the children to share their questions with each other and pinpoint the most frequently asked, the most unusual, and the most interesting questions.

Invite the children to attempt to answer their questions by themselves at first, so that their own explanations, logic and mistaken beliefs can be revealed and explored. Then you can provide them with factual information or sources of information, and any new and relevant vocabulary they need, such as:

nicotine	drug	absorb
tar	stimulate	addiction
lungs	effects	exhale
pregnant	baby	affect
unborn	inhale	substance

Invite the children to think about the reasons for smoking and not smoking, and emphasise the importance of making an informed healthy choice.

The activities which identify, clarify and extend what the children know about smoking can be used to explore the abuse of alcohol, dangerous inhalants and other mood-changing substances, or drugs, and the effects of accepted stimulants such as tea and coffee. These activities could also be used when exploring the theme of pressure and choice.

To enable children to make an informed decision about smoking, it is necessary that they explore:

- The social pressures and influences connected with smoking, such as,

    - peer group pressure;

    - adult and parental influences;

    - media influences.

- The biological and physiological consequences of smoking, such as,

    - short term effects;

    - long term effects;

    - effect on appearance and relationships.

There are **cross-curricular links** with science and environmental studies.

Substance abuse

 Being aware of the pressures and influences on me, particularly those concerned with the substances I take into my body. Who, and what can persuade me? When and how can I be persuaded? How can I learn to cope and make my own decisions?

Activity 1 ● *What are the pressures and influences?*

- Devising an advertising campaign. Examining strategies for persuading people. Recognising hidden messages.

- Group activities with opportunities for sharing and for family work.

Invite the class to pretend they are an advertising agency which has been commissioned to plan advertising campaigns to sell a range of goods such as:

– a fizzy drink.

– a once-a-week toothpaste.

– a perfume for pets.

– An old shoe belonging to someone famous, which is to be sold in aid of charity.

Children could prepare for this by looking at advertisements on television and in magazines. They could analyse the strategies behind the advertisements by asking questions such as:

– Who is the target of the advertisement? Grown-ups? Children?

– What promises do they make?

– What don't they tell you?

– What sorts of people, characters and music do they use?

– Would you buy the product? Why?

Invite the children to get into groups and begin planning their advertising campaign, starting with a television commercial.

Talk with the groups about:

– target audiences. Who would be most likely to buy the product? What kind of advertising would appeal to them? Should the advertisement use real people or cartoons?

– slogans and jingles.

– colour, scenery and background music.

– the hidden messages in advertising, for example:
'Drink this and you will be one of the crowd.'
'Clean your teeth with this and you will be much more attractive.'
'Rich and famous people have perfumed cats and dogs – now you can too.'
'If you buy this shoe you will become famous and help this charity.'

Suggest that the groups talk to each other about their plans and ask each other's opinion. Would they buy their product? Would the target group buy it?

Make a note of the vocabulary which they might find useful, such as:

client	research
customer	influence
market	disguise
persuade	communicate
target	

Come together as a class to display and present the campaign material and summarise what the children have learned from this activity, for example,

– Advertisements persuade you to buy something.

– They contain hidden messages which you should recognise.

– You should think carefully about it and make your own decision.

Activity 2 ● *Making my own decisions about harmful substances*

● Comparing advertising techniques with other pressures. Discussing and analysing the strategies used to pressurise children into taking risks. Using role-play.

● Class and group activities with an opportunity for family involvement.

Recall the activity on advertising campaigns and selling methods.

Ask the children to consider the ways in which people, television, magazines, comics and newspapers persuade them to do things such as: take risks, try harmful substances, believe that harmful substances don't really harm them.

Find similarities between advertising strategies and other 'persuaders'. Think about the persuasive strategies which might be used by peers or older children.

Explore with the children how it feels to be under this kind of pressure. What is the easiest thing to do or to say? What is the most difficult thing to do or to say?

Help the children to think of coping strategies which help one:

— to gain time.

— not to feel threatened.

— to stand by one's own feelings and decisions.

Emphasise the importance of knowing the facts (from reliable sources).

Encourage groups of children to plan role-play situations in which they could practise making decisions and standing by them. Invite the groups to write up the role-plays they have devised as playlets and share them with other groups.

Family involvement and support is very important in this type of activity.

These are **cross-curricular links** with topic work, investigations and media studies.

Classroom strategies and activities – A summary

In all the activities described earlier in the book there is considerable emphasis on active, rather than passive, learning. Children are very much encouraged to share their perceptions, and to take responsibility for recording, interpreting and communicating both these perceptions and their new learning. In line with this approach, group activities are also very much encouraged where the groups vary frequently in size and membership, although at the same time it is very important to value each child's contribution.

The following list summarises the major strategies and activities used in each age range.

1 *Talking, telling, listening and sharing*

These are ways of encouraging children to share and make sense of what they know and what they are learning. They give children opportunities to:

– explain, question and reflect, to link action to outcome;

– pretend and imagine;

– summarise, generalise and build up their own evaluation frameworks. It is important that teachers, or other adults involved, listen and respond to the children in a way that will encourage them and increase their confidence and skill in speaking aloud.

2 *Writing*

Children can use writing to:

– express, explain and internalise experience and new learning;

– share and communicate with others;

– reinterpret learning at a more personal level.

Writing activities with 4–11 year olds might include:

– children's invented writing;

– using the teacher as writer/consultant;

– sharing the writing task with others;

– writing 'by oneself'.

We need to remember that for the child the activity of writing can be very demanding or even threatening, especially when tackled alone. To ask children to do some writing as a way of reinforcing something they have just learnt may be a self-defeating activity: if the technical difficulties of writing are too demanding for the child, he or she will only concentrate on the writing and not on the health content. If you, or another adult, can act as 'scribe' for a child, or a group of children, the problem can be solved.

3 ● *Creative interpretation*

This strategy encourages children to interpret aspects of healthy lifestyles in personal ways, for example,

— painting, drawing and modelling;

— music, movement and drama;

— wall stories, collages, 'class books' and other activities which can be displayed and shared with others including the family.

4 ● *Presentation and display*

Children's work, can be presented:

— temporarily, as a way of collecting together and recording the children's learning;

— more permanently, to facilitate reflection, reinforcement, revision and as a starting point for further activity;

— in children's personal workbooks and files;

— as posters, invitations and news items;

— as wall stories and charts;

— on display boards, blackboards, flipcharts and display tables.

There are various ways of using:

— headings, titles, labels and messages to provide a focus or commentary to displayed work in order to generate further involvement;

— speech bubbles to pinpoint and highlight key messages.

The more children are involved in deciding what should be displayed, how it should be presented, what writing should be included and how to condense all the messages of a theme into one telling phrase, the more effective the learning will be.

5 ● *Classroom play and role-play*

These strategies provide children with a safe practice ground for exploring:

— their own and others' lifetyles as they see them;

– health related situations and problems with a range of outcomes;

– risk-taking and its possible outcomes.

6   ●   *Children's literature*

Stories and poems can often be used as starting points for exploring health related themes, enabling children to:

– learn about their own, and other people's relationships and experiences, the critical moments in situations, and the ways in which problems are resolved;

– experience a wider language of feelings and relationships.

7   ●   *Scientific and mathematical activities*

Scientific experiments can be used to help children explore specific aspects of health, for example, investigating the effects of heat and cold on food, or on the body, or measuring the pulse rate before and after exercise. Mathematics has a role to play in the presentation and analysis of the results of investigations and surveys. These activities provide a more formal way for children to develop skills such as observing, sorting, categorising, analysing, recording and summarising.

8   ●   *Becoming an expert – passing on the message*

Children, as individuals or groups, can gain by explaining their work to other children, teachers, their family or visitors, and passing on the key health messages they have identified as they have worked through a theme. Children draw on and practice different skills when they take on the role of expert. Their motivation and confidence increase as they focus on explaining and passing on the message; self-esteem is built up and learning consolidated.

9   ●   *Family involvement*

Keeping families informed of, and actively involved in, their children's health education is an important way of securing the children's acceptance of classroom work. It needs to become a much more regular part of primary school teaching and it also strengthens the partnership between home and school.

Appendices

Appendix 1
The draw and write investigation technique

This classroom technique was originally devised as part of the Health Education Authority's Primary School Project. It is based on drawing and writing activities and can be adapted for use with children aged 4 and over. The children themselves can help in the analysis of the responses. It can be used not only to discover how far children's perceptions and explanations have developed but also as one way of monitoring changes in their perceptions as they work through the programme you have planned.

● *How to organise the draw and write activity*

Introduction

- Ask the children to think about what they do to make, and keep, themselves healthy, but not to talk about it, among themselves.

- Ask the children to draw pictures of themselves doing things which make and keep them healthy. They are to draw as many of these pictures as they can on one side of a piece of paper (this makes analysis quicker and easier).

- Ask them to write (or dictate to you) a caption to accompany each picture.

- Only if there is time after they have finished drawing and writing can they colour their pictures.

Timing

The activity should be completed in one session. This can vary from 20–30 minutes depending on the age of the class.

Secrecy

To ensure the accuracy of the results, it is important that what the children produce is, as far as possible, their own unaided work. This is why you should prevent them from sharing their ideas. One way of explaining this is to tell them that what they are doing is a secret activity, and if they need to ask you for help, they should whisper to you so no one else hears. You can tell older children that they are taking part in a survey.

Spelling

If undue emphasis is placed on spelling this may detract from, or prolong, the activity in hand. It is recommended that:

– the children do not use word books to check words they cannot spell;

– they spell as they think words should be spelled, or

– you write for them the words or phrases they need, and

– you only write on the blackboard the phrases 'make me healthy' and 'keep me healthy'.

Labelling

Label each child's paper with their name and age to make analysis easier.

Materials

One A4 sheet of plain paper per child. Pencils and crayons.

● *How to explain the activity to the children*

Spoken instructions	Permitted prompts and reminders	Beware
Introduction 'Good morning/Hello. How are you all today? Good. I think you all look very well and *very healthy*. Let me have another look at you. Show me how healthy you are. Yes you're a very healthy looking class.'	Emphasise the word *healthy*. (Children will usually sit up, look taller and smile.) Try looking healthy yourself!	Please don't use any other words, for example, *fit and healthy*, *strong*, or *feeling good*.
Activity !: explanation 'Now I want you to have a good think about all the things you do that *make you healthy* and *keep you healthy*. No – don't tell me or anyone else. Keep as a secret inside your head the things you do to *make you healthy* and *keep you healthy*.'	Repeat the key phrases: *'make you healthy, keep you healthy'* as often as necessary. Encourage the children to join in and repeat them with you. Keep reminding them to 'Keep it a secret'.	Don't give any clues or hints. Don't let the children divulge their ideas to others.
Activity 2: drawing 'Now I want you to go to your places and draw yourself looking *healthy* and doing all the things you thought of that *make you healthy* and *keep you healthy*. If you're not sure how to start, draw yourself looking healthy and then think of the things you do that *make you healthy*.	Keep reminding them to 'Keep thinking of lots of pictures to draw'. Repeat the key phrases again. Praise children who have started, for example, 'Yes, that makes you healthy', 'That's a good one'. If necessary say, 'Try thinking of things you do each day'.	Discourage children from looking at each others' work and discussing their drawing. Don't suggest what to draw. Beware of children copying each other.
Activity 3: writing 'Now write what you are doing in your picture. You can whisper to me any spellings you need help with. If you can't write I'll come round and write for you. You tell me in a whisper what you want written and I'll write it for you'.	Where the spoken or written words seem to have no clear reference to health, for example, 'playing', or 'coming to school', ask the child 'How does that make you healthy?' Write down the child's answer, and if it is unrelated to health please write down *unrelated*.	Don't suggest to the child how his picture might be linked to health. Ask only the permitted questions.
Conclusion 'We have to stop in five minutes. I'm coming round for a last look. Colour in your pictures'.	Remind them 'Make sure you have drawn all the things that you thought of'.	Check that there is something written for each picture each child has drawn.

● How to analyse the results

You can use the following categories to code and analyse each child's work. On each child's paper make a note of, or code, the categories you think are illustrated and written about. At the end of this exercise you should have a better insight into the connection children make between their actions and their health, and into what they perceive as being healthy.

Main coding categories

- Exercise.

- Sleep.

- Temperature: keeping warm or cool, wearing appropriate clothing.

- Hygiene: getting washed, having a bath or shower, going to the lavatory, avoiding germs, keeping food protected.

- Play: games and toys (not games in the sense of organised physical activity).

- Safety: keeping oneself safe, looking out for dangers, dangerous objects, situations.

- Rest.

- Work (mental activity): doing school work, in particular reading and writing.

- Food and drink.

- Dentist, doctor: visiting or being visited by these.

- Relationships: being with special people, for example, family, playing with best friends, being cared for, loved, loving and caring for people, pets, having fun.

- Negative instructions: don't smoke, drink, cough on people.

- Fresh air – including going out in the sunshine.

- Medication: taking medicine, pills, tonics, plasters.

- Teeth – and cleaning one's teeth.

- Nil, or an inappropriate response.

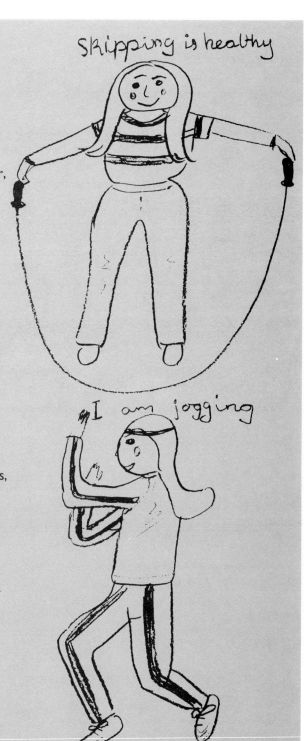

You may wish to analyse the children's responses *within* each category, for this you can use the suggested sub-categories below:

Main category	*Sub category*
Exercise	Press-ups, jogging, weightlifting, walking, games, cycling, swimming, gymnastics, dancing.
	Other activities can be coded as 'exercise general'.
Sleep	General category only.
Temperature	Wearing appropriate clothing, keeping cool.
	Other activities can be coded as 'temperature general'.
Hygiene	Washing, bathing, food preparation, avoiding germs.
	Other activities can be coded as 'hygiene general'.
Play	Hobbies.
	Other activities can be coded as 'play general'.
Keeping safe	On the road, in or near water, in the house, being responsible, cautious.
	Other activities can be coded as 'keeping safe' general.
Rest	General category only.
Work	School work.
	Other activities can be coded as 'work general'.
Food and Drink	Fruit, vegetables, dairy food, food labelled as 'good', drinks, milk.
	Other activities can be coded as 'food and drink general'.
Dentist, doctor	Visiting the dentist, visiting the doctor, going to the health centre, going to hospital.
	Other activities can be coded as 'dentist general', 'doctor general'.
Relationships	General category only.

Negative instructions	Not coughing on people, not smoking, not getting too hot or too cold, not picking up germs, not eating fat, not eating sugar.
	Other activities can be coded as 'negative instructions general'.
Fresh air	Being out in the sun.
	Other activities can be coded as 'fresh air general'.
Medication	Having vitamins, being vaccinated or injected.
	Other activities can be coded as 'medication general'.
Teeth	Using a toothbrush.
	Other activities can be coded as 'teeth general'.

Appendix 2

Resources

The books, videos and television programmes listed below are just a small selection from the many useful resources available. You will no doubt accumulate your own collection of materials, many children's books can be used in the context of work on 'health'.

As well as consulting teachers' centres and local libraries, you can contact your local Health Education Unit or 'Health Promotion Unit'. This may be listed under the name of your health authority in the phone book but if you cannot find it, contact the Liaison Section of the Health Education Authority or ask at your local Community Health Centre or local library. This service is normally run by Health Education Officers and generally includes advisory services, the loan of materials and the supply of Health Education Authority publications.

The Health Education Authority offers a subscription service to individuals and organisations concerned with Health Education. Subscribers receive a copy of the *Health Education Authority's Annual Report*, copies of the *Health Education News*, published bi-monthly, a copy of the *Library List and Journal Articles of Interest to Health Educators*, and a copy of each new leaflet and poster as published.

The Health Education Authority also supplies *Books for Children 5–8: an annotated bibliography with relevance to health education*, and *Teaching Aids for children 5–8: an annotated list with relevance to health education*. These lists are also available for ages 9–13. These are available free of charge from the Information Centre, Health Education Authority, Hamilton House, Mabledon Place, London WC1H 9TX.

Information on drug and alcohol abuse can be obtained from the Teachers' Advisory Council for Alcohol and Drug Education, 3rd Floor, Furness House, Trafford Road, Salford M5 2XJ, or from The Institute of Drug Dependence, 1–4 Hatton Place, Hatton Garden, London EC1N 8ND.

Me and looking after myself

Teacher's books and resources

Ourselves (Learning Through Science) Roy Richards and Doug Kincaid (Schools Council/Macdonald Education, 1981)
Pupil workcards and a Teacher's Guide full of ideas for finding out about the body through practical activities.

Me Barking and Havering and Essex Health Education Depts (P.H. Promotions Craigmoor, Brompton, Cumbria).
Cards for ages 6–8.

The Good Teeth Programme (HEC/Drake Educational Associates, 1986)
Cards, games and books for children under 5.

Natural Nashers Hemming Prevention Aids
A life-size set of teeth.

Your Children's Teeth Health Education Authority (booklet)
Explains what parents can do to help make sure their children's teeth and gums are healthy.

What to do about glue-sniffing Health Education Authority (booklet)
Advice on the misuse of glue and other solvents.

Food: a Resource for Learning in the Primary School (ILEA Learning Resources 1979).

Children in Hospital (ILEA Learning Resources 1983)
Teacher's notes, 3 photographic sequence sets and a hospital workbook. Devised to help prepare children for a visit to hospital. Contains useful suggestions for activities with primary schoolchildren of all ages and abilities. Accompanies the ILEA video 'Hospital Story – Children in Hospital'.

Health Education – Drugs and the Primary School Child HEA/TACADE, (Teachers' Advisory Council for Alcohol and Drug Education 1986)
A curriculum package for the use with 9–11 year-olds consisting of an introductory unit, a module for teachers, a module for parents and a module for pupils, plus 61 slides. The pack aims to create awareness amongst pupils, teachers and parents of drugs, and their use and abuse.

Books for children

The Body Book Claire Rayner (Piccolo, 1979)
Where do I come from? What does dying mean? What does my heart do? The answers to these and many other questions about the human body and how it works.

Hearing
Seeing
Smiling and Tasting
Henry Pluckrose (Franklin Watts, 1985)
A series of four books with good quality colour photographs for nursery and infant level, with simple text.

Hearing
Seeing
Tasting and Smelling
Touching
Nigel Snell (Hamish Hamilton, 1983)
An amusing illustrated series providing basic information.

What happens when you eat?
What happens when you breathe?

What happens when you grow?
What happens when you listen?
What happens when you run?
What happens when you talk?
Joy Richardson (Hamish Hamilton, 1984)
Information books with indexes and suggested activities.

Dog so Small Philippa Pearce (Puffin Books, 1970)
Ben longs for a dog and open spaces for exercise and adventure. For better readers.

The Sleep Book Dr Seuss (Collins, 1964)
Each person dropping off to sleep is ticked off in an enormous sleep machine.
What happens when you sleep?
What happens when you catch a cold?
What happens when you hurt yourself?
Joy Richardson (Hamish Hamilton 1983/4)

If you knew Nicky Peter Wilson and Sandra Irvine (Angus & Robertson, 1983)
Nicky is autistic and goes to a special school. Anna, his sister, narrates this tale, pointing out some of the difficulties he makes, but sympathy and love are shown.

I can't hear like you Althea Braithwaite (Dinosaur, 1985)
Looking at hearing problems.

I can't talk like you Althea Braithwaite (Dinosaur, 1982)
The Association for Speech Impaired Children helped produce this account of a child's experience trying to speak and to remember.

I have asthma Althea Braithwaite (Dinosaur, 1982)
An asthma sufferer describes his daily life and answers other children's questions in a very matter-of-fact way.

I have diabetes Althea Braithwaite (Dinosaur, 1983)
The reality of the daily insulin injection, blood sugar level testing and regular clinic visits for a little girl. Diabetes is treated as a nuisance, nothing more.

I use a wheelchair Althea Braithwaite (Dinosaur, 1983)

Me and my relationships

Teacher's books and resources

Startline Schools Council Moral Education 8–13 Project (Longman Group, 1978)
The aim of the pack is to encourage children to develop greater social awareness, to appreciate the needs and feelings of others and to acquire basic social skills. The pack is made up of many separate items, including stories, posters, workcards and a handbook.

Kids Can Say No! Rolf Harris video (Rolf Harris Video Ltd., 1985) (Also available from CFL Vision-Concord Films Council Ltd. for hire and purchase).

A 20 minute video for 5–11 year-olds aimed at preventing child sexual abuse. Four abusive incidents are acted, ranging from approaches by strangers to sexual advances by the father, and the children talk about what to do – say 'No', get away fast and tell someone you trust. The video comes with teaching notes and two books – *Preventing Child Sexual Assault* by Michele Elliott, and *Sexual Abuse Within the Family* by the CIBA Foundation. Asterisks appear at the bottom of the screen when suitable points to break for discussion occur.

Preventing Child Sexual Assault Michele Elliott (Bedford Square Press/NCVO, 1985)
A helpful starter and 'confidence booster' for anyone wishing to tackle this crucial subject in school or at home. Michele Elliott gives practical advice on teaching children about their right to be safe. She also suggests what to do if abuse is suspected or occurs, and gives a list of organisations to turn to for further support.

Child Abuse: an educational perspective ed. Peter Maher (Blackwell, 1987)

Feeling Yes, Feeling No Video by the National Film Board of Canada (Educational Media International/Concord Films Council Ltd., 1984)
A video in four sections, three for children and one for adults. Total running time 71 mins. Aimed at any educator concerned about the prevention of sexual abuse of children.

Personal and Social Skills Nigel Leech and Arthur D. Wooster (Religious and Moral Education Press, 1986)
A book of activities for children.

School Sex Education: Why, what and how? Doreen Massey (The Family Planning Association, 1988).

Sex Education: Some Guidelines for Teachers by D J Went (Bell and Hyman, 1985)

Sex Education BBC Enterprises (Film Hire and Purchase) (BBC, 1983)
Three programmes: 'Growing Someone New', 'Life Begins' (each 20 minutes)

What Shall We Tell the Children? Peter Moyle (W.H. Allen, 1979)
About divorce.

Books for children

Badger on the Barge Janni Howker (Heinemann Educational Books New Windmills, 1987).

A baby in the family Althea Braithwaite (Dinosaur, 1981)
For parents to read to children about the arrival of a new baby.

Jane is Adopted Althea Braithwaite (Souvenir Press, Brightstart Series, 1980)
A straightforward book about adoption that will help families discuss the topic openly.

George and the Baby Althea Braithwaite (Dinosaur, 1973)
A dog feels rejected, thereby expressing the feelings other children have when a new baby arrives.

My New Family Althea Braithwaite (Dinosaur, 1984)
The transfer from a home to being fostered reveals for the first time to a primary school girl that families can have rows without splitting up.

Peter Pig Althea Braithwaite (Dinosaur, 1973)
Peter finds that people who look different can still be friends.

Smith, The Lonely Hedgehog Althea Braithwaite (Dinosaur, 1977)
Smith is shy and lonely, but eventually finds a friend.

It's Your Turn Roger Susanna Gretz (Armada, 1986)
Humourous book about a little pig learning about taking turns.

Moving Molly Shirley Hughes (Armada, 1981)
A little girl moves house, but soon finds new friends.

My Naughty Little Sister Dorothy Edwards (Magnet, 1982)
A Mother's stories, told to her children about the little sister of her childhood.

Trouble with Jack Shirley Hughes (Corgi, Picture Series, 1986)
The trouble with Nancy's brother Jack was that he was not a tidy person at all, but she had to learn to put up with him whatever he was like.

No More Secrets for Me Oralee Wachter (Puffin, 1986)
Four stories with a multi-cultural background, about preventing child abuse. Provides a list of helpful organisations.

The Anti-Colouring Book Susan Striker and Edward Kimmel (Hippo Books, 1984)

Titch Pat Hutchins (Picture Puffin, 1974)
Titch was the smallest in the family. He had a big sister and an even bigger brother, and everything they had seemed bigger and better, until Titch planted a seed that grew, and grew.

The Owl Who was Afraid of the Dark Jill Tomlinson (Puffin, 1973)
Positive and humorous treatment of the fear of darkness.

Diwali Chris Deshpande
Sam's Passover Lynne Hannigan
Dat's New Year Linda Smith
(Black, Celebration series, 1985)
Celebrations from other cultures seen through the eyes of young children.

Kausar at Home
Shakoor is Born
Praying with Ammi
Going to Mosque School

Ramadan
Eid-ul-Fitr
City Links Series June Jones (Blackie, 1986)
A series of Muslim stories, checked by the UK Islamic Mission.

Me and my community and environment

Teacher's books and resources

Exploring your Neighbourhood: Along the Way (ILEA Learning Resources, 1980)
This pack contains a teacher's book and 3 sets of 5 activity cards, and VHS videocassette (for hire or purchase.) These materials are designed to provide a framework which can be used to study any urban environment. Children are encouraged to look closely at the streets they use on their journey to school, and to use simple fieldwork techniques to gather information.

Exploring Your Neighbourhood: Round our Way (ILEA Learning Resources, 1980)
A Teacher's Book and VHS videocassette, for hire or purchase.

Children and Traffic (Macmillan)
A pack of books and cards

Safety at Home and School Chris North for Science Horizons: West Sussex Science 5–14 Scheme (Macmillan Education, 1984)
A 46–page, A4 book consisting of loose-leaf sheets in a slide binder, with information for the teacher followed by 'activity sheets' which can be photocopied. *Safety at Home and School* is from Level 2a of the Science Horizons Scheme and is designed for use with 7–11 year olds. The aims of the unit are to make pupils safety-concious at home and school, to highlight dangers and help children avoid accidents, and to teach safe use of tools and apparatus.

Play it Safe (Health Education Authority, 1987)
How to prevent accidents to babies, toddlers and young school-age children. Includes what to do in an emergency and basic first-aid.

Smoking and Pollution Family Smoking Project (Health Education Authority, 1988)
Pupils' booklet, parents' leaflet, teachers' guide. Promotes discussion about the effects of smoking on health, other people, the atmosphere and developing countries.

Books for children

How We Live Anita Harper (Kestrel, 1977)
Do you live in a house, or a flat, or perhaps a caravan? People live in all sorts of places.

Health Education – general teaching resources

Reference books

Health for Life 2 – Health Education in the primary school A teacher's guide to three key topics: The World of drugs, Keeping myself safe, Me and my *relationships.* The Health Education Authority's Primary School Project (Thomas Nelson and Sons Ltd, 1989)

Health Education in Schools Edited by K David and T Williams (Harper and Row Ltd. 1987)
Contains a chapter, 'Health Education in Primary Schools' by Noreen Wetton and Alysoun Moon.

Thinking about Personal and Social Education in the Primary School Edited by Peter Lang (Basil Blackwell, 1988)
Contains a chapter, 'Starting Where Children Are: health education in the primary school' by Noreen Wetton and Alysoun Moon.

Schools Council Health Education Project 5–13 (Thomas Nelson & Sons, 1977)
In two parts: *All about Me* (a teacher's guide for the 5–8 age range), and *Think Well* (a teacher's guide, spirit masters and resource sheets for the 9–13 age range).

Television programmes

Watch BBC 2
A series of five programmes for 5–7 year olds which aims to widen the experiences of young children and to stimulate project work. Individual programme titles are:

1 Skin and hair

2 Eyes and sight

3 Teeth and food

4 Ears and air

5 Taking care

Good health Central Independent Television
For 8–12 year olds. The aim of this series is to promote health education within the primary and middle school and to encourage children to take increasing responsibility for looking after themselves and each other.

1 Look after yourself	6 Germs, germs, germs	11 Help! (first aid)
2 Dr. Sweet-tooth	7 Exercise and rest	12 Jackie (a deaf girl)
3 Healthy eating	8 The great clean-up	13 Summer story
4 White ivory	9 Love your lungs	14 Drugs
5 Keeping safe	10 What next? (human reproduction)	

Sex Education BBC 2
For 8–10 year olds. Three programmes designed to help answer children's questions about the biology of sex and its human development. The programmes discuss growing up, the changes associated with puberty, pre-natal development, birth, conception and menstruation.

1 Growing

2 Someone new

3 Life begins

All year round Channel 4
A series to encourage the development of science and health education with children aged 6–8. Possible programmes of interest include:

3 Keeping safe

5 Death

10 Birth

14 Beginning again

Who – me? BBC 2
For the upper primary level. A series exploring some of the personal and social issues affecting children's lives. Each programme is a fictional drama based on children's experiences or a dramatic reconstruction of real events. Topics include moving home, family responsibilities and peer group pressures.

Whirligig Channel 4
For lower juniors. A unit in the summer term entitled 'Looking After Me' may contain programmes of relevance. Topics covered include health and hygiene; safety in the home, park, playground and streets; coping with the loss of a relative or friend; and saying 'No'.

Teacher's resources

The Good Health Project Trefor Williams, Noreen Wetton and Alysoun Moon (Forbes Publications Ltd, 1986)
A series of booklets containing teaching notes and photocopiable worksheets designed to accompany the Central TV Series.

Jimmy on the Road to Super Health! Health Education Group (Glasgow 1981)
Spiral-bound teachers' manual, spirit masters and resource sheets. A story (serialised in seven episodes). Each episode is followed by additional background information for the teacher. For 10–12 year olds.

Fit for Life Schools Council/HEC Project: Health Education for Slow Learners (Macmillan Education, 1983)
Worksheets and teachers' notes for 9–13 year olds. Designed for slow learners, these materials are an extension of *All About Me* and *Think Well. Fit for Life* aims to foster positive self-esteem, to encourage the development of decision-making skills and to help young people cope with the physical and mental changes which occur as they grow.

My Body A Health Education Council Project (Heinemann Educational Books 1983)
Workcards, games pack, teacher's book.
A curriculum project for 10–12 year olds, designed to help pupils learn about their bodies and explore various aspects of human biology and health care. Contains a strong anti-smoking element.